Modern Biology®

Study Guide
Answer Key

HOLT, RINEHART AND WINSTON

A Harcourt Education Company

Orlando • Austin • New York • San Diego • Toronto • London

To the Teacher

The *Modern Biology* Study Guide is designed to help students focus on the key concepts and terminology presented in each section of each chapter of their textbook. The *Modern Biology* Study Guide Answer Key is designed to help teachers quickly, efficiently, and easily check the answers to each of the Study Guide worksheets. To help accomplish this task, the answer key for each section uses the same structure and numbering as the worksheet it checks.

ISBN 0-03-036717-4

14 1186 20 19 18 17

4500686881

Section 1-1

VOCABULARY REVIEW

1. Development is the process involving cell division and cell differentiation by which an organism becomes a mature adult.
2. Reproduction is the process by which an organism produces new organisms like itself.
3. An organ is a structure that carries out a specialized job inside an organ system.
4. A tissue is a group of cells in an organ that have similar abilities and that allow the organ to function.

MULTIPLE CHOICE

1. c   2. b   3. d   4. b   5. a

SHORT ANSWER

1. A cell is the smallest unit that can perform all of life's processes.
2. Sample answer: An owl maintains its body temperature by burning fuel to produce body heat and by fluffing up its feathers to trap an insulating layer of air next to its body.
3. Sample answer: By studying biology, you can make informed decisions on issues that impact you and society, such as environmental issues, health, and technology.
4. Bacteria reproduce asexually by splitting in two. Frogs reproduce sexually by producing sperm and eggs. One sperm and one egg combine to form a single cell that divides many times to produce a new frog.
5. Rocks are not composed of cells, do not have internal systems for maintaining homeostasis, and do not contain hereditary information in the form of DNA.

STRUCTURES AND FUNCTIONS

The buffaloes and grass are all composed of cells (cells). Different types of cells compose the different tissues in the buffaloes (organization). The grass uses energy from the sun to manufacture food, and the buffaloes consume the grass for their food (energy use). The buffaloes have hair to help maintain their internal environment (homeostasis). The calf will eventually grow into a full-grown buffalo (growth). Buffalo increase their herds through reproduction.

Section 1-2

VOCABULARY REVIEW

1. A domain is one of three major subdivisions of organisms that can be divided into one or more kingdoms.
2. Diversity of life describes the variety of different kinds of living things. Unity of life describes the features that living things have in common.
3. Adaptations are traits that improve an individual's ability to survive and reproduce. Evolution is the process in which a population changes over time due to increased reproduction of organisms with certain adaptations.
4. An ecosystem is a community of living things and their physical environment. Ecology is the branch of biology that studies how organisms interact with each other and with their environments.

MULTIPLE CHOICE

1. d   2. b   3. d   4. c   5. d

SHORT ANSWER

1. Animals produce carbon dioxide and water, which is needed by plants. Accept all reasonable answers.
2. If an adaptation is not inherited, future generations of organisms will not have the favorable trait and evolution cannot occur.
3. Natural selection is the process by which organisms that have certain favorable traits are better able to survive and reproduce successfully than organisms that lack these traits.
4. Two organisms that share the same kingdom must also share the same domain because kingdoms are subdivisions of domains.
5. This trait will not spread through the population. Since the frog produces no eggs, it will have no offspring to inherit the trait.

STRUCTURES AND FUNCTIONS

The deer eat the grass and get energy and nutrients from the grass. The panther kills and eats the deer, getting energy and nutrients from the deer and the grass.

Section 1-3

VOCABULARY REVIEW

1. A prediction is what is expected to happen if a hypothesis were true.
2. A control group is a normal standard against which to compare an experimental group.
3. A dependent variable is a factor that is measured in a controlled experiment.
4. An independent variable is a factor that distinguishes the control and experimental groups in a controlled experiment.
5. A theory is a set of related hypotheses that have been confirmed and that explain a great amount of data.

MULTIPLE CHOICE

1. c   2. b   3. c   4. a   5. d

SHORT ANSWER

1. Quantitative data are data that can be measured in numbers. Examples include the dimensions of an object, the number of objects in a group, and the duration of an event.
2. The validity of the research is checked by experts in the field.
3. A prediction is a statement made in advance that declares the results that will be obtained from testing a hypothesis in an experiment, if the hypothesis is true.
4. They might use statistics to determine relationships between variables, compare the data with those obtained in other studies, and determine possible sources of experimental error.
5. The control group should have consisted of rats that were injected with the same type of salt solution but without the drug. The dependent variable was blood pressure, and the independent variable was the drug.

STRUCTURES AND FUNCTIONS

Observations:	Inferences:
The owl is sitting in a tree.	Owls can fly.
The owl has a mouse in its beak.	Owls have binocular vision.
The owl has sharp talons.	Owls hunt at night.

Section 1-4

VOCABULARY REVIEW

1. *Light electron* does not belong; the other three are types of microscopes.
2. *Base unit* does not belong; the other three are parts of a light microscope.
3. *Mass density* does not belong; the other three are characteristics of microscopes.
4. *Minute* does not belong; the other three are SI base units.
5. *Meter* does not belong; the other three are SI derived units.

MULTIPLE CHOICE

1. d   **2.** b   **3.** c   **4.** a   **5.** c

SHORT ANSWER

1. light source, specimen, objective lens, ocular lens
2. LM, about 2,000×; TEM, 200,000×; SEM, 100,000×
3. m, km, cm, mm, μm. 1 km = 1,000 m; 1 cm = 0.01 m; 1 mm = 0.001 m; 1 μm = 0.000001 m
4. They should use a TEM, since it has the magnification necessary to view viruses and, unlike an SEM, can reveal structures that are inside cells.

STRUCTURES AND FUNCTIONS

a, ocular lens (eyepiece); b, nosepiece; c, objective lenses; d, stage; e, light source

Section 2-1

VOCABULARY REVIEW

1. An atom is the simplest particle of an element that retains all of the properties of that element.
2. A neutron is a nuclear particle that has no electrical charge.
3. A compound is a substance that is made up of atoms of two or more elements in fixed proportions.
4. A covalent bond is an attachment between two atoms that share one or more pairs of electrons.
5. An ion is an atom or molecule with an electrical charge.

MULTIPLE CHOICE

1. b   **2.** a   **3.** d   **4.** c   **5.** a

SHORT ANSWER

1. Mass is the quantity of matter an object has, while weight is a measure of the pull of gravity on mass.
2. BO_2, 1 boron and 2 oxygen atoms; $C_6H_{12}O_6$, 6 carbon, 12 hydrogen, and 6 oxygen atoms; KCl, 1 potassium and 1 chlorine atom; NH_3, 1 nitrogen and 3 hydrogen atoms
3. The oxygen atoms share two pairs of electrons, since each atom needs two more electrons to fill the orbitals of its outermost energy level.
4. Argon will not tend to form bonds with other elements. With an atomic number of 18, argon must have 18 electrons: 2 in the first energy level, 8 in the second, and 8 in the third. Since the orbitals of its outermost energy level is filled, argon is chemically stable.

STRUCTURES AND FUNCTIONS

1. A covalent bond is formed between hydrogen and chlorine atoms.
2. A hydrogen atom and a chlorine atom share one electron. This process gives the hydrogen atom a full orbital of 2 electrons. The chlorine atom will

have full orbitals corresponding to its three energy levels of 2, 8, and 8 electrons.

Section 2-2

VOCABULARY REVIEW

1. In a chemical reaction, a reactant is the starting substance and a product is the ending substance. Reactants are shown on the left side of an equation and products are shown on the right side.
2. A catalyst reduces the amount of activation energy needed to start a reaction. An enzyme serves as a catalyst in the reactions of living things.
3. In an oxidation reaction, a reactant loses one or more electrons; in a reduction reaction, a reactant gains one or more electrons.

MULTIPLE CHOICE

1. b   **2.** c   **3.** d   **4.** a   **5.** b

SHORT ANSWER

1. Reactants: $C_{12}H_{22}O_{11}$, H_2O, Products: $C_6H_{12}O_6$, $C_6H_{12}O_6$
2. By reducing the activation energy that is needed for a reaction, a catalyst allows the reaction to proceed spontaneously or with the addition of a small amount of energy.
3. It indicates that the reaction can proceed in either the forward or the reverse direction.
4. Cl is reduced; Na is oxidized.
5. The reaction proceeds slowly because the activation energy is high. An enzyme or other catalyst is needed to lower the activation energy and speed up the reaction.

STRUCTURES AND FUNCTIONS

1. energy needed without a catalyst
2. energy needed with a catalyst
3. There is a net release of energy. Energy of the products is less than energy of the reactants.

Section 2-3

VOCABULARY REVIEW

1. A solvent is a substance in which a solute is dissolved.
2. An aqueous solution is a solution in which water is the solvent.
3. A hydroxide ion is a negatively charged ion consisting of one oxygen atom and one hydrogen atom, OH^-.
4. A base is a solution that contains more hydroxide ions than hydronium ions.
5. A buffer is a chemical substance that neutralizes small amounts of either an acid or a base added to a solution.

MULTIPLE CHOICE

1. c   **2.** b   **3.** a   **4.** c   **5.** d

SHORT ANSWER

1. Adhesion allows water to stick to a dry surface.
2. Solutions can be mixtures of liquids, solids, or gases.
3. The solution contains 10 g of sugar, and the solvent is water.
4. Acidic: more H_3O^+ ions than OH^- ions. Alkaline: more OH^- ions than H_3O^+ ions. Neutral: equal number of H_3O^+ and OH^- ions.
5. The solution with a pH of 9 has 10^6, or 1,000,000, times more hydroxide ions.

6. By neutralizing small amounts of acid or base that may be added to a solution, buffers keep pH values at normal and safe levels. The control of pH is essential for the function of enzymes.
7. Since a tenfold increase in H_3O^+ ion concentration reflects a decrease of one pH unit, a 100-fold increase in concentration reflects a decrease of two pH units. Therefore, the new pH would be 5.5.

STRUCTURES AND FUNCTIONS

Drawings should show two water molecules below and one above the central water molecule. The molecules below should have their H atoms facing away from the central molecule, and the molecule above should have one of its H atoms pointing toward the central molecule. Dashed lines should be drawn between each H atom in the central molecule and the O atom in each of the lower water molecules, and between the O atom in the central molecule and the nearer H atom in the upper water molecule.

Section 3-1

VOCABULARY REVIEW

1. An organic compound is a compound containing carbon atoms covalently bonded to other carbon atoms and to other elements. Examples: any carbon-containing compound, such as benzene, ethanol, glycerol, glucose, fructose, sucrose, ATP, and ADP.
2. A functional group is a cluster of atoms in a compound that influences the properties of that compound. Examples: hydroxyl group, phosphate group.
3. An alcohol is an organic compound with a hydroxyl group attached to one of its carbon atoms. Examples: ethanol, methanol, glycerol.
4. A monomer is a simple molecule that can bond to others of its kind to form more complex molecules. Examples: glucose, fructose.
5. A polymer is a complex molecule that consists of repeated, linked units. Example: DNA, proteins.

MULTIPLE CHOICE

1. a   2. c   3. b   4. a   5. d

SHORT ANSWER

1. The hydroxyl group on alcohols is polar, and this makes alcohols polar compounds. Alcohols can therefore form hydrogen bonds.
2. carbon atom, monomer, polymer, macromolecule
3. The glucose molecule releases a hydroxide ion, OH^-, and the fructose molecule releases a hydrogen ion, H^+. These two ions combine to produce water, H_2O.
4. The hydrolysis products are ADP and inorganic phosphate. Energy is released.
5. With seven electrons in its outermost energy level, carbon could not form double or triple bonds with other atoms, so far fewer organic compounds could be formed.

STRUCTURES AND FUNCTIONS

1. Forward reaction: reactants, glucose and fructose; products, sucrose and H_2O. **2.** condensation reaction **3.** Reverse reaction: reactants, sucrose and H_2O; products, glucose and fructose. **4.** hydrolysis

Section 3-2

VOCABULARY REVIEW

1. A monosaccharide is a simple sugar containing carbon, hydrogen, and oxygen in a ratio of 1:2:1; a polysaccharide is a complex molecule composed of three or more monosaccharides.
2. An amino acid is a compound containing carbon, hydrogen, oxygen, and nitrogen. A protein is a large polymer of amino acids.
3. A nucleotide is a compound containing a phosphate group, a five-carbon sugar, and a ring-shaped nitrogen base; a nucleic acid is a very large polymer of nucleotides.

MULTIPLE CHOICE

1. c   2. a   3. d   4. b   5. d

SHORT ANSWER

1. The storage form is glycogen, and the quick-energy form is glucose. Glycogen consists of hundreds of glucose molecules linked in a highly branched chain.
2. Starch, 1; proteins, 20.
3. Phospholipid composes most of the cell membrane. The hydrophobic tails of the phospholipids provide a barrier between the inside and outside of the cell.
4. Steroids are lipids made of four fused carbon rings. Examples: testosterone and cholesterol.
5. Wax serves as a waterproof layer, limiting water loss and preventing insects from drying out.

STRUCTURES AND FUNCTIONS

a, substrate; b, enzyme; c, products

Section 4-1

VOCABULARY REVIEW

1. A cell is the smallest unit that can carry on all of the processes of life.
2. The cell theory states that all living organisms are made of one or more cells, that cells are the basic units of structure and function, and that cells come only from the reproduction of existing cells.

MULTIPLE CHOICE

1. c   5. d
2. a   6. d
3. c   7. a
4. b

SHORT ANSWER

1. (1) All living things are composed of one or more cells. (2) Cells are the basic units of structure and function in an organism. (3) Cells come only from the reproduction of existing cells.
2. Information about cells could not be understood and organized into a central theory until microscope technology had improved and accurate observations were made.
3. The cork cells that Hooke observed were the remains of dead plant cells. The material from the inside of the cells had been lost or destroyed.
4. You would know that it was made of cells and the cells reproduce to make more cells.

STRUCTURES AND FUNCTIONS

1. Approximately 200 years elapsed between the discovery of cells in 1665 and the observation of mitochondria in muscle cells in 1857.
2. The third part of the cell theory was added in 1855. This was 190 years after cells were discovered.

Section 4-2
VOCABULARY REVIEW

1. An organelle is a cell component that performs specific functions for the cell.
2. The nucleus is an organelle that contains coded information in the form of DNA for regulating functions and reproduction and directs most of the activities of the cell.
3. A eukaryote is an organism whose cells contain a membrane-bound nucleus and other organelles.
4. A prokaryote is an organism that lacks a nucleus and membrane-bound organelles.

MULTIPLE CHOICE

1. a   2. b   3. a   4. d

SHORT ANSWER

1. Its flat platelike shape covers and protects the body's surface.
2. Just as organs carry out the organism's life functions, organelles maintain the life of the cell.
3. Eukaryotic cells have a membrane-bound nucleus and membrane-bound organelles.
4. The surface area increases by a factor of 100. The volume increases by a factor of 1,000.

STRUCTURES AND FUNCTIONS

1. a, prokaryotic cell; b, eukaryotic cell. 2. Features: eukaryotic cell has a nucleus and other membrane-bound organelles, but the prokaryotic cell does not; prokaryotic cell is smaller. 3. X, nucleus; Y, cell membrane

Section 4-3
VOCABULARY REVIEW

1. The nucleoplasm is the jellylike liquid that fills the nucleus. The nuclear envelope is a double membrane that surrounds the nucleus.
2. The cytoskeleton is the network of tubes and filaments that give a cell its shape and serves as tracks for the movement of organelles in the cell. Microtubules are one of three structural elements that make up the cytoskeleton.
3. Both are hairlike organelles that extend from the surface of a eukaryotic cell, but cilia are shorter and are present in larger numbers on a cell.

MULTIPLE CHOICE

1. d   2. a   3. c   4. b   5. c

SHORT ANSWER

1. Some proteins form channels or pores through which certain substances can pass. Other proteins bind to a substance on one side of the membrane and carry it to the other side.
2. Ribosomes are made of proteins and RNA. They are involved in protein synthesis.
3. The cytoskeleton is a network of long protein strands located in the cytosol. Three major components are microfilaments, microtubules, and intermediate filaments.

4. Cilia and flagella are composed of nine pairs of microtubules arranged around a central pair.
5. The detergent would cause the cells to disintegrate because it would break up the plasma membrane as well as organelle membranes, all of which are largely composed of lipid.

STRUCTURES AND FUNCTIONS

a. mitochondrion; b. nucleus; c. nucleolus; d. Golgi apparatus; e. rough endoplasmic reticulum; f. ribosome

Section 4-4
VOCABULARY REVIEW

1. A cell wall is a rigid layer that lies outside the plasma membrane of a plant cell.
2. A plastid is an organelle that is surrounded by a double membrane and contains DNA.
3. Thylakoids are flattened membranous sacs that contain chlorophyll.
4. Chlorophyll is a green pigment that absorbs light and captures energy for a plant cell.
5. A central vacuole is a large, fluid-filled organelle that stores water, enzymes, and wastes in plant cells.

MULTIPLE CHOICE

1. b   2. b   3. a   4. c   5. c

SHORT ANSWER

1. Primary cell walls are assembled on the surface of the plasma membrane while the cell is growing. They can grow as the cell grows. Secondary cell walls are produced after the cell has stopped growing. Secondary cell walls cannot expand.
2. Plant cell walls are made of cellulose embedded in proteins and carbohydrates. Cell walls help support and protect the plant.
3. When water is plentiful, the central vacuole expands. The other organelles are pushed against the plasma membrane in a thin layer.
4. The nucleoid is not surrounded by a membrane and is therefore not a nucleus. Bacteria do not have an internal membrane system or membrane-bound organelles.

STRUCTURES AND FUNCTIONS

a, Golgi apparatus; b, cell wall; c, vacuole; d, nucleus; e, nucleolus; f, mitochondrion; g, ribosome; h, chloroplat; i, endoplasmic reticulum

Section 5-1
VOCABULARY REVIEW

1. A difference in the concentration of molecules in two areas, called a concentration gradient, can result in diffusion, the movement of molecules from the area of higher concentration to the area of lower concentration.
2. Osmosis is the diffusion of water molecules across a cell membrane. When osmosis results in water molecules entering a plant cell, the molecules exert a pressure against the cell wall, called turgor pressure.
3. A hypertonic solution has a higher solute concentration than the cytosol of a cell. In a hypertonic solution a plant cell will lose water and shrink away from the cell wall, a process called plasmolysis.

MULTIPLE CHOICE

1. d   2. b   3. a   4. c   5. b

SHORT ANSWER

1. At equilibrium, the movement of molecules continues, but because there is no concentration gradient, there is no net movement in any particular direction.
2. Carrier proteins bind to a molecule of the substance on one side of the membrane, change shape, transport the molecule across the membrane, and release the molecule on the other side.
3. The stimuli are stretching of the cell membrane, electrical signals, and chemicals in the cytosol or external environment.
4. Both involve the binding of a specific substance to a particular kind of protein and a change in shape of the protein as the process (transport or chemical reaction) proceeds. After the process is completed, the protein is unchanged.

STRUCTURES AND FUNCTIONS

a, hypotonic; b, hypertonic; c, isotonic; d, hypertonic; e, isotonic; f, hypotonic

Section 5-2
VOCABULARY REVIEW

1. Active transport is the movement of materials across a membrane from an area of lower concentration to an area of higher concentration.
2. Endocytosis is the process by which cells ingest external fluid, macromolecules, and large particles.
3. A vesicle is a membrane-bound organelle that pinches off from the cell membrane during endocytosis or fuses with the cell membrane during exocytosis.
4. Phagocytosis is a type of endocytosis in which cells ingest large particles or whole cells.

MULTIPLE CHOICE

1. b   2. a   3. c   4. b   5. d

SHORT ANSWER

1. The mechanism uses energy to move (pump) Na^+ and K^+ up their concentration gradients.
2. The phagocyte forms a pouch in its cell membrane and engulfs bacteria in the pouch. It then pinches off the pouch to form a vesicle. Lysosomes fuse with the vesicle, and lysosomal enzymes destroy the bacteria it contains.
3. Proteins are made on ribosomes and packaged into vesicles by the Golgi apparatus. The vesicles move to the cell membrane and fuse with it, releasing the proteins from the cell through exocytosis.
4. The interior of the lipid bilayer is nonpolar and therefore would repel ions, which are attracted to polar environments.

STRUCTURES AND FUNCTIONS

1. The correct order is d, c, f, b, a, e. 2. Na^+ ions are released on the external side of the cell membrane.
3. K^+ ions are released on the cytosolic side of the cell membrane.

Section 6-1
VOCABULARY REVIEW

1. Grana are stacks of thylakoids inside a chloroplast; the stroma is the solution that surrounds the thylakoids.
2. Carotenoids are accessory pigments that assist chlorophyll a in capturing light energy during photosynthesis.

3. Chemiosmosis is the process by which ATP is made during photosynthesis. The production of ATP is catalyzed by the enzyme ATP synthase.

MULTIPLE CHOICE

1. a   2. c   3. d   4. b   5. d

SHORT ANSWER

1. Photosynthesis involves many chemical reactions linked such that the product of one reaction is consumed in the next reaction.
2. Chloroplasts have an inner membrane system consisting of thylakoids. The pumping of protons into the thylakoids builds up a proton concentration gradient across the thylakoid membrane.
3. The energy-carrying products are ATP and NADPH.
4. They help chlorophyll a capture light energy by absorbing energy in wavelengths that chlorophyll a cannot absorb. This enables the photosynthetic cell to capture more of the energy in light.
5. Photosystem II most likely evolved first, because it replaces electrons lost from chlorophyll a with electrons from water. Since photosystem I accepts electrons from photosystem II, it probably evolved after photosystem II.

STRUCTURES AND FUNCTIONS

a, electrons; b, NADPH; c, ATP; d, H^+

Section 6-2
VOCABULARY REVIEW

1. The Calvin cycle is a biochemical pathway that produces a three-carbon sugar from carbon dioxide during photosynthesis.
2. Carbon fixation is the incorporation of carbon dioxide into organic compounds.
3. A stoma is a small pore on the surface of a plant through which water, O_2, CO_2, and other gases enter or leave the plant.
4. The C_4 pathway is a carbon fixation pathway in which CO_2 is incorporated into four-carbon compounds.
5. The CAM pathway is a carbon fixation pathway in which CO_2 is incorporated into organic compounds at night and released to enter the Calvin cycle during the day.

MULTIPLE CHOICE

1. a   2. c   3. d   4. b   5. d

SHORT ANSWER

1. In each turn of the cycle, three molecules of ATP and two molecules of NADPH are used.
2. $CO_2 + H_2O \xrightarrow{\text{light energy}} (CH_2O) + O_2$
3. CAM plants open their stomata at night, whereas C_3 and C_4 plants open their stomata during the day.
4. Increasing the temperature initially accelerates the various chemical reactions involved in photosynthesis. At higher temperatures, many of the enzymes that catalyze these reactions become ineffective, and the stomata begin to close.
5. The stomata would open. That would allow more CO_2 to enter the leaf from the surrounding air, stimulating photosynthesis.

STRUCTURES AND FUNCTIONS

Clockwise from the top: 3 CO_2, 6 3-PGA, 6 ATP, 6 ADP, 6 NADPH, 6 $NADP^+$, 6 G3P, 3 ATP, 3 ADP, 3 RuBP

Section 7-1

VOCABULARY REVIEW

1. Cellular respiration is the process in which cells make ATP by breaking down organic compounds.
2. Glycolysis is a biochemical pathway in which one molecule of glucose is oxidized to two molecules of pyruvic acid.
3. Lactic acid fermentation is an anaerobic pathway in which pyruvic acid is converted into lactic acid.
4. Alcoholic fermentation is an anaerobic pathway in which pyruvic acid is converted into ethyl alcohol and CO_2.

MULTIPLE CHOICE

1. a   2. c   3. d   4. b   5. c

SHORT ANSWER

1. The fermentation pathways can operate in the absence of oxygen.
2. The energy-containing products are NADH, ATP, and pyruvic acid.
3. These pathways regenerate NAD^+, which the cells can use to keep glycolysis going to make more ATP in the absence of oxygen.
4. Without niacin or the ability to make it, the person would be deficient in NAD^+. Since NAD^+ is used in Step 3 of glycolysis, glycolysis would be inhibited.

STRUCTURES AND FUNCTIONS

a, glucose; b, glycolysis; c, pyruvic acid; d, lactic acid fermentation; e, alcoholic fermentation; f, lactic acid; g, ethyl alcohol

Section 7-2

VOCABULARY REVIEW

1. Aerobic respiration is the set of pathways in cellular respiration that require oxygen to break down pyruvic acid.
2. The mitochondrial matrix is the space inside the inner membrane of a mitochondrion.
3. The Krebs cycle is a biochemical pathway that breaks down acetyl coenzyme A, producing CO_2, hydrogen atoms, and ATP.
4. FAD, or flavine adenine dinucleotide, is a molecule that accepts electrons during redox reactions.

MULTIPLE CHOICE

1. b   2. c   3. a   4. d   5. c

SHORT ANSWER

1. Most of the energy is acquired by NADH; three molecules are produced during each turn of the cycle.
2. The reactions of the electron transport chain occur in the inner mitochondrial membrane.
3. $C_6H_{12}O_6 + 6O_2 \rightarrow 6CO_2 + 6H_2O + energy$
4. The mitochondrial membranes segregate the enzymes and reactants of the Krebs cycle, facilitating the reactions they participate in. The folding of the inner mitochondrial membrane provides a large surface area for the molecules of the electron transport chain. The area between the inner and outer mitochondrial membranes provides a confined space in which protons can accumulate, driving chemiosmosis.

STRUCTURES AND FUNCTIONS

a, protons; b, protons; c, protons; d, NAD^+; e, $FADH_2$; f, O_2; g, ADP + phosphate

Section 8-1

VOCABULARY REVIEW

1. Histones help maintain the shape of a chromosome and aid in the tight packing of DNA; nonhistone proteins control the activity of specific regions of DNA.
2. A chromatid is one-half of a chromosome; a centromere is the area of a chromatid that holds the two chromatids in a chromosome together.
3. A sex chromosome is a chromosome that determines the sex of an organism; an autosome is any other chromosome.
4. A diploid cell has both chromosomes in each homologous pair; a haploid cell has only one chromosome in each homologous pair.

MULTIPLE CHOICE

1. d   2. b   3. a   4. c   5. a

SHORT ANSWER

1. Histones help coil and package the DNA into a very small volume.
2. Homologous chromosomes are the same size and shape and carry genes for the same traits.
3. The picture is called a karyotype. If it shows two X chromosomes, the person is a female; if it shows one X and one Y chromosome, the person is a male.
4. Relatively simple organisms with more chromosomes might have smaller chromosomes containing less DNA. Also, some of the DNA in an organism's chromosomes may not carry information that is actually used by the organism.

STRUCTURES AND FUNCTIONS

a, chromosome; b, centromere; c, chromatids; d, homologous chromosomes, or homologues

Section 8-2

VOCABULARY REVIEW

1. *Telophase* does not belong; it is a phase of mitosis, and the other three are phases of interphase.
2. *Interphase* does not belong; it is a phase of the cell cycle, and the other three are phases of mitosis.
3. *Binary fission* does not belong; it pertains to prokaryotes, and the other three pertain to eukaryotes.
4. *Spindle fiber* does not belong; it pertains to nuclear division, and the other three pertain to cytoplasmic division.
5. *Vesicles* does not belong; vesicles are organelles, some of which participate in cytoplasmic division, and the other three are involved in nuclear division.

MULTIPLE CHOICE

1. c   2. b   3. d   4. a   5. c

SHORT ANSWER

1. G_1 phase: the cell grows. S phase: DNA is copied. G_2 phase: the cell prepares for cell division. Mitosis: the nucleus divides. Cytokinesis: the cytoplasm divides.
2. Prophase: the chromatin coils and forms chromosomes, the nucleolus and nuclear envelope disappear, and the mitotic spindle forms. Metaphase: kinetochore fibers move the chromosomes to the cell equator. Anaphase: the chromatids in each chromosome separate and move toward opposite poles of the cell. Telophase: the mitotic spindle disappears, the chromatids unwind to form chromatin, the nuclear envelope reforms, and a nucleolus appears.

3. Vesicles formed by the Golgi apparatus fuse at the midline of the cell to form the cell plate, a cell wall that elongates to separate the cell into two cells.
4. Without a G_1 growth phase, the cells would not grow to their mature size after cytokinesis. Therefore, the offspring cells would become smaller with each cell cycle.

STRUCTURES AND FUNCTIONS

a, telophase; b, metaphase; c, prophase; d, anaphase

Section 8-3
VOCABULARY REVIEW

1. Oogenesis is the production of mature egg cells, or ova.
2. A tetrad is a pair of homologous chromosomes lined up next to each other during prophase I of meiosis.
3. Independent assortment is the random separation of homologous chromosomes during anaphase I.
4. Polar bodies are haploid offspring cells produced by meiosis during oogenesis.

MULTIPLE CHOICE

1. d   2. c   3. a   4. b   5. c

SHORT ANSWER

1. Genetic recombination occurs during crossing-over and independent assortment.
2. Prophase I: DNA coils into chromosomes, the nucleolus and nuclear envelope disappear, the mitotic spindle forms, and synapsis and crossing-over occur. Metaphase I: the tetrads line up randomly along the midline of the cell, and spindle fibers attach to the centromere of each homologue. Anaphase I: the homologues move toward opposite poles of the cell. Telophase I: the chromosomes reach the opposite ends of the cell, and cytokinesis begins.
3. In meiosis I, the offspring cells are haploid but each cell contains two copies of the chromosome because the original cell copied its DNA before meiosis I. The offspring cells of meiosis II are also haploid, but each cell contains only one copy of the chromosome because, unlike meiosis I, the cells do not copy their DNA before meiosis II.
4. The advantage of asexual reproduction is that offspring are genetically identical to their parent, so if the parent is well adapted to its environment, the offspring will also be well adapted. The disadvantage of asexual reproduction is that without genetic recombination, the offspring lack the variability that would allow some to survive if the environment became less favorable to their survival.

STRUCTURES AND FUNCTIONS

a, anaphase II; b, metaphase I; c, anaphase I; d, metaphase II

Section 9-1
VOCABULARY REVIEW

1. The F_1 generation consists of the offspring of a cross between two parents; the F_2 generation consists of the offspring of a cross between two individuals in the same F_1 generation.
2. A dominant factor is one that masks the effect of another factor for the same characteristic; a recessive factor is one whose effect is masked by another factor for the same characteristic.

3. Self-pollination occurs between flowers on the same plant. Cross-pollination occurs between flowers on different plants.

MULTIPLE CHOICE

1. c   2. a   3. d   4. b

SHORT ANSWER

1. An *allele* is each of two alternative forms of a gene.
2. In meiosis, the two alleles of each gene are segregated when the two chromosomes in each pair of homologues are separated into different gametes. Alleles of genes located on different chromosomes or far apart on the same chromosome assort independently when homologues are randomly separated during meiosis.
3. Orange flower color is dominant. All of the F_1 plants will have orange flowers.
4. Mendel would have observed that the traits controlled by dominant factors for these characteristics almost always appeared together. Thus, he might not have concluded that the factors for different characteristics are assorted independently.

STRUCTURES AND FUNCTIONS

Possible combinations are *RB*, *Rb*, *rB*, and *rb*.

Section 9-2
VOCABULARY REVIEW

1. In complete dominance, heterozygous and dominant homozygous individuals have the same phenotype. For example, in pea plants, the *P* allele is completely dominant over the *p* allele, so both *PP* and *Pp* plants have purple flowers.
2. In incomplete dominance, neither allele is completely dominant over the other and both influence the phenotype. For example, in four o'clocks, neither the *R* nor *r* allele is completely dominant, so *Rr* plants have pink flowers.
3. In codominance, neither allele is dominant or recessive; both are expressed in heterozygotes. For example, in MN blood blood types, both M and N molecules are produced by an $L^M L^N$ individual.

MULTIPLE CHOICE

1. b   2. a   3. c   4. d   5. c

SHORT ANSWER

1. In a homozygous individual, both alleles of a pair are the same; in a heterozygous individual, the two alleles of a pair are different.
2. 0.25×80 individuals = 20 individuals
3. *AA* and *Aa* will result. 100% will have the dominant phenotype.
4. In a testcross, the dominant phenotype would appear in all of the offspring if the cow were homozygous dominant but in only about 50% of the offspring if the cow were heterozygous. With only one individual per F_1 generation, distinguishing between these two possibilities would take a long time, until a calf with the recessive phenotype was born.

STRUCTURES AND FUNCTIONS

Arrangements of the offspring alleles will vary according to the order of the parental alleles in the Punnett square. **1.** 9/16 **2.** 1/4 **3.** 1/16 **4.** 1/16

Section 10-1

VOCABULARY REVIEW

1. A virulent strain of a bacterium is one that causes disease.
2. Transformation is the transfer of genetic material from one cell to another cell or from one organism to another organism.
3. A bacteriophage is a virus that infects bacteria.

MULTIPLE CHOICE

1. a   **2.** c   **3.** d   **4.** a   **5.** b

SHORT ANSWER

1. to show that live *R* cells are not virulent
2. to show that live *S* cells are virulent and can kill a mouse
3. to show that heat-killed *S* cells do not cause disease
4. to show that something in the heat-killed *S* culture was acting on the live *R* cells to kill the mouse; experiment 3 showed that it was not the killed *S* cells themselves that killed the mouse.
5. The slippery capsule prevents the cells of the defense system from capturing and destroying the bacterial cells.

STRUCTURES AND FUNCTIONS

1. Experiment 2
2. Experiment 1

Section 10-2

VOCABULARY REVIEW

1. A purine is a nitrogenous base with two rings of carbon and nitrogen atoms. Examples may include adenine or guanine.
2. A pyrimidine is a nitrogenous base with one ring of carbon and nitrogen atoms. Examples may include cytosine or thymine.
3. A complementary base-pair is a pair of nitrogenous bases connected to each other by hydrogen bonds. Examples may include adenine-thymine and cytosine-guanine.
4. A nitrogenous base is a base in DNA containing nitrogen and carbon.

MULTIPLE CHOICE

1. c   **2.** d   **3.** a   **4.** b   **5.** b

SHORT ANSWER

1. The three parts are a deoxyribose sugar, a phosphate group, and a nitrogenous base. The phosphate group and the base are connected to different parts of the sugar.
2. Since guanine and cytosine are complementary, another 15% of the nucleotides must contain cytosine. The remaining 70% of the nucleotides (100%–30%) must contain adenine and thymine in equal proportions (35% each), since they are complementary to each other.
3. Complementary base pairing is important because the hydrogen bonds between the bases hold the two strands of DNA together and because it serves as a way for DNA to replicate.
4. The X-ray diffraction photographs showed that the shape of the DNA molecule was a double helix.

STRUCTURES AND FUNCTIONS

a, deoxyribose; b, guanine; c, adenine; d, phosphate group

Section 10-3

VOCABULARY REVIEW

1. A replication fork is a Y-shaped region that results when the two strands of DNA separate during replication.
2. A helicase is an enzyme that separates the strands of DNA during replication.
3. Semi-conservative replication produces a new DNA molecule with one original strand and one new strand.

MULTIPLE CHOICE

1. b   **2.** a   **3.** b   **4.** d   **5.** c

SHORT ANSWER

1. Replication occurs simultaneously at many origins along the DNA.
2. Producing exact copies ensures that when a cell divides, the offspring cells will receive the same genetic information as the parent cell.
3. Cancer can result when errors occur in the replication of DNA in genes that control how a cell divides. A mass of cancerous cells called a tumor can result.
4. The hydrogen bonds break easily, making it easier for the two strands in the molecule to separate during replication. The strong covalent bonds ensure that the sequence of nucleotides remains fixed in each strand.

STRUCTURES AND FUNCTIONS

Part a: helicase enzymes separate DNA strands;
Part b: DNA polymerase enzymes add complementary nucleotides to each original strand of DNA and covalent bonds form between adjacent nucleotides;
Part c: DNA polymerases finish replicating DNA and fall off, two DNA molecules identical to original DNA molecule have formed.

Section 10-4

VOCABULARY REVIEW

1. A codon is a sequence of three mRNA nucleotides that codes for a specific amino acid or a start or stop signal.
2. Translation is the process of assembling polypeptides from information encoded in mRNA.
3. An anticodon is a sequence of three tRNA nucleotides that pairs with a specific codon.

MULTIPLE CHOICE

1. a   **2.** d   **3.** b   **4.** b   **5.** b

SHORT ANSWER

1. The anticodons are UAC, GUA, CGU, and UCA. (The last three nucleotides in the mRNA sequence are a stop codon, which has no anticodon.) The polypeptide will initially contain four amino acids.
2. The tRNA that pairs with the start codon on mRNA carries methionine.
3. RNA contains ribose; DNA contains deoxyribose. RNA usually contains uracil in place of thymine. RNA is single stranded; DNA is double stranded.
4. All of the codons from the deletion point to the end of the transcript would be shifted by one nucleotide, so the sequence of amino acids specified from that point on would be different. Translation would terminate prematurely if the shift resulted in a new stop codon before the end of the transcript.

a, polypeptide or protein; b, peptide bond;
c, amino acid; d, tRNA; e, anticodon; f, codon; g, mRNA
or transcript; h, ribosome

Section 11-1
VOCABULARY REVIEW

1. A regulator gene is a prokaryotic gene that codes for the production of a repressor protein, which inhibits the transcription of one or more structural genes.
2. An operator is a DNA segment that controls the access of RNA polymerase to the promoter. An operon is the DNA segment that contains an operator, promoter, and structural genes.
3. An intron is a section of a structural gene that is transcribed but not translated. An exon is a section of a structural gene that is transcribed and translated.
4. A transcription factor is a protein that facilitates gene transcription by binding to RNA polymerase and to an enhancer.

MULTIPLE CHOICE

1. c   2. d   3. a   4. b   5. d

SHORT ANSWER

1. An operon is a series of genes that code for specific products and the regulatory elements that control those genes. Operons have been found mostly in prokaryotes.
2. Lactose binds to the repressor protein, which causes the repressor protein to be released from the operator site. This permits the RNA polymerase to transcribe the structural genes.
3. In the absence of lactose, the repressor protein binds to the operator site; this inhibits the RNA polymerase from transcribing the structural genes.
4. Without a nuclear envelope, there is no structure to segregate newly synthesized RNA from ribosomes. Therefore, ribosomes can begin to translate the RNA as soon as it is formed, before it has had a chance to be modified.

STRUCTURES AND FUNCTIONS

1. a, regulator gene; b, lactose, or inducer; c, repressor protein; d, promoter; e, operator.
2. If the regulator gene were deleted then the repressor protein could no longer be produced. Without a repressor protein at the operator site, RNA polymerase would transcribe structural genes continuously.
3. Transcription is activated because the lactose molecule has bound to the repressor protein. This causes the repressor protein to release from the operator site, which then permits RNA polymerase to transcribe the structural genes.

Section 11-2
VOCABULARY REVIEW

1. A homeotic gene is a regulatory gene that determines where anatomical structures will form. A homeobox is a specific nucleotide sequence within a homeotic gene that regulates patterns of development.
2. A proto-oncogene is a gene that regulates cell growth, cell division, and the ability of cells to adhere to one another. An oncogene, formed when a proto-oncogene mutates, causes uncontrolled cell division.

3. A sarcoma is a cancer of bone or muscle tissue; a lymphoma is a cancer of the tissues that form blood cells.
4. An oncogene causes uncontrolled cell proliferation; a tumor-suppressor gene prevents it.

MULTIPLE CHOICE

1. a   2. d   3. a   4. b   5. d

SHORT ANSWER

1. Homeotic genes code for regulatory proteins that are thought to control the rate of cell division in various body areas by switching genes on or off. These variations in cell division produce specific patterns of structural development.
2. Factors include the person's age, number of exposures to carcinogens, amount of carcinogen in each exposure, and possibly a genetic predisposition to certain types of cancer.
3. Viruses can introduce oncogenes into a host cell, activate the host cell's own oncogenes, or cause mutations in the host cell's proto-oncogenes or tumor-suppressor genes.
4. Two key characteristics of cancer cells include uncontrolled growth and metastasis.
5. Cancer is a disease in which cells grow and undergo mitosis at an abnormally high rate. If the genes that control the cell cycle and the mechanism of that control were better understood, the causes of cancer would also be better understood. Perhaps cancer could be slowed or cured if the cell cycle of cancerous cells could be modified.

STRUCTURES AND FUNCTIONS

left box, regulate cell growth; middle box, cancer; right box, prevention of uncontrolled cell division

Section 12-1
VOCABULARY REVIEW

1. A sex chromosome contains genes that determine an individual's sex. An autosome is a chromosome that is not directly involved in determining sex.
2. A germ-cell mutation occurs in one of an organism's gametes; a somatic-cell mutation occurs in one of the other cells in an organism's body.
3. Translocation occurs when a chromosome piece breaks off and attaches to a nonhomologous chromosome; nondisjunction occurs when homologues fail to separate during meiosis, so that one gamete receives both homologues.
4. A deletion is a loss of a piece of chromosome due to breakage. An inversion occurs when a broken piece of chromosome is reattached backwards.
5. In a substitution, one nucleotide in a codon is replaced with a different one; in a frameshift mutation, the loss or addition of a nucleotide causes the remaining codons to be incorrectly grouped.

MULTIPLE CHOICE

1. b   2. a   3. c   4. d   5. a

SHORT ANSWER

1. The male parent determines the offspring's sex. Offspring that receive an X chromosome from the male parent will be female; those that receive a Y chromosome will be male.

2. Morgan crossed a white-eyed male with a female homozygous for red eyes, and then crossed members of the F_1 generation resulting from the first cross. He found that all of the white-eyed flies in the F_2 generation were male.
3. Crossing-over during meiosis causes homologous chromosomes to exchange alleles, resulting in new combinations of alleles in the offspring.
4. A frameshift mutation would have a more serious effect if it occurred near the beginning of a gene, since it would change nearly all of the codons in the gene. The resulting protein likely would be nonfunctional.

STRUCTURES AND FUNCTIONS

white eyes (map unit number 1), vermilion eyes (31), miniature wings (34)

Section 12-2
VOCABULARY REVIEW

1. skin color, eye color, height, or hair color
2. ABO blood groups
3. Huntington's disease
4. pattern baldness

MULTIPLE CHOICE

1. d   2. c   3. d   4. a   5. b

SHORT ANSWER

1. Pattern baldness is controlled by the allele B. Testosterone interacts with the heterozygous genotype (BB') to produce baldness. Since males have higher levels of testosterone, BB' males are more likely to lose their hair than BB' females.
2. A small sample is removed from the amniotic fluid surrounding the fetus or from the chorionic villi between the uterus and the placenta. Fetal cells in the sample are used to construct a karyotype, which may reveal chromosomal abnormalities.
3. A sex-influenced trait is influenced by the presence of sex hormones and its genes are not located on sex chromosomes, while a sex-linked trait is linked to a sex chromosome.
4. Children: type A, $I^A i$; type B, $I^B i$; type AB, $I^A I^B$; type O, ii. One parent is type A, $I^A i$; the other parent is type B, $I^b i$.

STRUCTURES AND FUNCTIONS

X-linked recessive trait: one filled square, one open square, one half-filled circle, and one open circle. Autosomal recessive trait: one half-filled square, one open square, one half-filled circle, and one open circle.

Section 13-1
VOCABULARY REVIEW

1. A DNA fingerprint is a pattern of bands on a photographic film, where the bands represent specific fragments from an individual's DNA.
2. Gel electrophoresis is a technique in which nucleic acids or proteins are separated according to size and charge as they migrate through a gel.
3. A probe is a radioactive segment of single-stranded DNA that is complementary to DNA fragments that have been selected for comparison.
4. A primer is a single-stranded sequence of DNA required for the initiation of replication in PCR.

MULTIPLE CHOICE

1. d   2. c   3. b   4. c   5. b

SHORT ANSWER

1. Radioactive probes bind to specific fragments in a DNA sample such as a donor gene. A probe can identify which bacteria contain recombinant DNA.
2. When only a very small amount of DNA is available, PCR can be used to produce enough copies of the DNA to make a DNA fingerprint.
3. Since each restriction enzyme recognizes a specific DNA sequence, only those DNA pieces that have been produced by the same restriction enzyme will have complementary sticky ends.
4. Answers could include: identifying human remains, determining a person's paternity, tracing human origins, provide evidence in criminal cases, improve food crops, determine susceptibility to genetic diseases, and provide treatments or cures for genetic disorders.

STRUCTURES AND FUNCTIONS

a, human gene; b, restriction enzyme; c, sticky ends; d, plasmid; e, recombinant DNA; f, recombinant bacterium

Section 13-2
VOCABULARY REVIEW

1. Proteomics is the study of all of an organism's proteins, including their identities, structures, interactions, and abundances.
2. Bioinformatics is the use of computers to investigate biological questions.
3. The 8 million SNPs in the human genome are unique spots where individuals differ by a single nucleotide.
4. The Human Genome Project is a research effort to sequence the entire human genome and locate all of the functionally important sequences.

MULTIPLE CHOICE

1. d   2. a   3. d   4. d   5. b

SHORT ANSWER

1. They wanted to learn the location of all the important genes in the genome in order to learn how the genome is organized, how gene expression and cell growth are controlled, and about human evolution.
2. Answers should include three of the following: Only about 2 percent of the human genome encodes proteins. Exons are not distributed equally on chromosomes. The human genome contains only about 30,000 to 40,000 genes. Exons are spliced to allow a gene to encode different proteins. Half the human genome arises from the shuffling of transposons. There are about 8 million SNPs.
3. It is the proteins, not the DNA, that carry out the work of cells. Scientists must understand proteins and how they work if they are to understand how genes work.

STRUCTURES AND FUNCTIONS

1. The more complex organisms generally have larger genomes than less complex organisms, but there are many exceptions.
2. If the genome is larger than expected for the number of genes, there might be large amounts of noncoding DNA present. If the genome is smaller than

expected for the number of genes, the size of the organism's proteins may be small, requiring fewer nucleotides.

Section 13-3
VOCABULARY REVIEW

1. A DNA vaccine is a vaccine that is made from the DNA of a pathogen but does not have disease-causing capability.
2. A telomere is a repeated DNA sequence at the end of a chromosome that shortens with each cell division.
3. Bioethics is the study of ethical issues related to DNA technology.
4. In gene therapy, a genetic disorder is treated by introducing a normally functioning gene into a patient's cells.

MULTIPLE CHOICE

1. c 2. a 3. d 4. b 5. a 6. a

SHORT ANSWER

1. A DNA vaccine contains DNA from a pathogen but cannot cause disease. When the vaccine is injected into a patient, the DNA directs the synthesis of a protein. Antibodies are produced by the body against the protein. If the patient contracts the disease in the future, the antibodies in his or her body will be able to provide protection.
2. Dolly suffered from premature aging and disease, possibly because the nucleus that produced her had chromosomes with shortened telomeres.
3. Although a normal gene is introduced into a patient's surface cells in the lung, these cells are not the ones that need to produce the highest levels of the missing transport protein. The virus carrying the normal gene cannot reach the deep lung cells where the normal gene is most needed.
4. Sample answer: Engineered traits such as herbicide resistance could transfer to weeds and create "superweeds."
5. Acceptable answers could include making plants that carry out photosynthesis at a higher rate, produce greater yields with less water or in warmer or colder climates, and produce crops that have a greater nutritional value, taste better, or look more appealing.

STRUCTURES AND FUNCTIONS

a and b: acceptable answers include medicines and organs that do not trigger rejection when transplanted into humans. Answers c, d, and e may include pest-resistant crops, herbicide-resistant crops, disease-resistant crops, and rice with higher nutritional value.

Section 14-1
VOCABULARY REVIEW

1. Biogenesis is the principle that all living things come from other living things.
2. Spontaneous generation is the supposed origin of living things from nonliving things.
3. Vital force was the force that according to supporters of spontaneous generation, caused life to appear spontaneously.

MULTIPLE CHOICE

1. b 2. c 3. a 4. b 5. c

SHORT ANSWER

1. Observations with the microscope revealed the existence of microorganisms that are simple in structure, numerous, and widespread. Investigators of that time concluded that microorganisms arise spontaneously from a "vital force" in the air.
2. Spallanzani reasoned that boiling the broth would kill all of the microorganisms in the broth, on the inside of the glass, and in the air inside the flask.
3. Instead of sealing the flask in the experimental group after boiling, Pasteur used a flask with a curved neck, which allowed air inside and outside the flask to mix but prevented microorganisms from entering the body of the flask.
4. Pasteur's experiment permitted air from the outside to mix with air from the inside, which would have allowed any "vital force" to enter and cause the broth to become cloudy if there were such a "vital force."
5. Believers in spontaneous generation could have argued that the meat Redi used was somehow unable to develop into maggots, regardless of whether flies were present or absent. The control group showed that this was not the case.

STRUCTURES AND FUNCTIONS

Control group: c, e, a. Experimental group, c, b, d.

Section 14-2
VOCABULARY REVIEW

1. A radioactive isotope is an isotope whose nucleus tends to release particles, radiant energy, or both; radioactive dating is a technique for determining the age of a material by measuring the amount of a particular radioactive isotope the material contains.
2. The release of particles, radiant energy, or both by a radioactive isotope is called radioactive decay; half-life is the time it takes for one-half of any size sample of a particular isotope to decay.
3. A microsphere is a spherical collection of many protein molecules organized as a membrane; a coacervate is a collection of droplets that are composed of different types of molecules, including amino acids and sugars. Both structures are cell-like and form spontaneously in the laboratory from simple organic molecules.

MULTIPLE CHOICE

1. d 2. c 3. b 4. a 5. a

SHORT ANSWER

1. Isotopes with short half-lives are most useful for dating relatively young rocks, while those with long half-lives are most useful for dating older rocks.
2. Some scientists think that the atmosphere of early Earth contained large amounts of CO_2, a gas that interferes with the production of organic compounds in laboratory simulations of proposed early-Earth conditions.
3. Their discovery showed that some aspects of cellular life can arise without direction from genes.
4. No, this method estimates the age of the oldest unmelted surface rocks on Earth. Since the surface of Earth probably melted many times as the planet was formed, the Earth should be older than these rocks.

STRUCTURES AND FUNCTIONS

An isotope content of 1/16 will occur after four half-lives; $4 \times 75,000$ years = 300,000 years.

Section 14-3
VOCABULARY REVIEW

1. A ribozyme is an RNA molecule that can act as an enzyme.
2. Chemosynthesis is the synthesis of organic compounds using energy contained in inorganic molecules.
3. Cyanobacteria are a group of photosynthetic unicellular prokaryotes.
4. Endosymbiosis is the mutually beneficial relationship that is hypothesized to have existed between large prokaryotes and the smaller prokaryotes that invaded them and eventually gave rise to mitochondria and chloroplasts.

MULTIPLE CHOICE

1. a   2. d   3. c   4. b   5. d

SHORT ANSWER

1. Each RNA molecule might have competed with slightly different RNA molecules for nucleotides. An RNA molecule that was more successful in getting nucleotides would have an advantage, and it would pass that advantage on to the new RNA molecules it created by replicating.
2. Ultraviolet radiation from the sun damages DNA, but the development of the ozone layer in the upper atmosphere prevented much of this radiation from reaching the surface of Earth, allowing life to exist on land.
3. Both organelles replicate independently of the cell, have circular DNA like that in prokaryotes, and contain genes that are different from those of the rest of the cell.
4. The pre-eukaryotic cells would have received protection from the damaging effects of oxygen, obtained the energy-containing products of aerobic respiration, and been able to harness the energy in sunlight. The small prokaryotes may have experienced a more stable environment inside the larger cell.

STRUCTURES AND FUNCTIONS

a, photosynthetic eukaryotes; b, aerobic eukaryotes; c, photosynthetic prokaryotes; d, chemosynthetic prokaryotes; e, heterotrophic prokaryotes

Section 15-1
VOCABULARY REVIEW

1. Evolution is the development of new types of organisms from preexisting types of organisms over time.
2. Natural selection is a process in which organisms best suited to their environment reproduce more successfully than other organisms.

MULTIPLE CHOICE

1. d   2. c   3. a   4. d   5. c

SHORT ANSWER

1. Since acquired traits are not genetically determined, they cannot be passed on to offspring. Therefore, they cannot cause a population to change over generations.
2. Darwin extended Malthus' ideas to populations of all organisms and reasoned that the environment limits the populations of all organisms by causing deaths or limiting births.

3. Evolution is the change of populations of organisms over time; natural selection is the mechanism by which evolution occurs.
4. Lamarck would have said that the ancestors of modern-day giraffes had short necks but stretched their necks as they tried to reach leaves in trees; so, their descendants were born with longer necks. Darwin would have said that in a population of ancestral giraffes, some had slightly longer necks than others; the long-necked giraffes were better able to feed on tree leaves and as a result produced more offspring. Over time, the proportion of long-necked giraffes in the population increased.

STRUCTURES AND FUNCTIONS

The bird in B appears to have greater fitness, since it has produced more offspring.

Section 15-2
VOCABULARY REVIEW

1. A homologous structure is an anatomical structure that occurs in different species and originated by heredity from a structure in a common ancestor; analogous structures have closely related functions but are not derived from the same ancestral structure.
2. A fossil is the evidence or remains of a preexisting organism; the principle of superposition states that if a sequence of sedimentary rock strata have been undisturbed, the oldest strata will be at the bottom of the sequence and younger strata will be on top. The relative age of the strata is usually determined by comparing the fossils contained in the strata.
3. The relative age of a fossil or rock is simply an indication of whether the fossil or rock is younger or older than another fossil or rock; the absolute age of a rock is the rock's age in years.

MULTIPLE CHOICE

1. b   2. c   3. b   4. a   5. a

SHORT ANSWER

1. A biologist would concentrate on homologous features, since they originated in a shared ancestor.
2. The animal evolved from an ancestor in which that structure was functional.
3. In biogeography studies, similar animals that seem to be closely related are adapted to different environments in nearby areas. Also, in areas that are widely separated animals that seem to be unrelated are observed to have similar adaptations to similar environments in the separate areas.
4. Fossils show that a group of organisms, such as marine mammals, have changed over time to adapt to different environments.
5. The environment will not select for or against organisms that have a particular structure unless that structure affects the organisms' fitness.

STRUCTURES AND FUNCTIONS

a, youngest fossil; b, mammal fossils; c, first dinosaurs; d, first land plants; e, trilobites; f, oldest fossil

Section 15-3
VOCABULARY REVIEW

1. the evolution of Caribbean anole lizards
2. Examples may include different breeds of dogs, cats, cattle, or food crops.

3. some flowers and insects; animals and microbes
4. the evolution of Caribbean anole lizards with similar adaptations on separate islands
5. Two examples are the evolution of the Galápagos finches and the evolution of domestic dogs.
6. evolution of resistance to pesticides by insect populations, of plants to herbicides, and evolution of resistance to antibiotics by disease-causing bacteria

MULTIPLE CHOICE

1. b   2. c   3. a   4. d   5. a

SHORT ANSWER

1. Adaptive radiation occurs when a new population in a new environment, such as an island, undergoes divergent evolution until the descendant populations fill many parts of the environment.
2. Answer will vary, but could include the lizards moving to an area where the trees are still healthy, or they could adapt to live in another part of the environment, such as living in small shrubs or on the ground. The lizards could also go extinct if they could not move to another area or adapt to the new environment.
3. Answers will vary, but could include domestic dogs, domestic cats, cattle, sheep, and pigs for animals and corn, wheat, fruit trees, such as apples or oranges, and flowers, such as roses or orchids.
4. The long-lived species would be more likely to become extinct after a sudden environmental change. The short-lived species, with large numbers of offspring, would be more likely to adapt to the changing environment. The short-lived species can adapt more easily because of the larger pool of genetic variations available in the larger population.

STRUCTURES AND FUNCTIONS

divergent evolution; approximately 16 million years ago; the galago

Section 16-1

VOCABULARY REVIEW

1. Population genetics is the study of evolution from a genetic point of view.
2. A gene pool is the total genetic information available in a population.
3. Allele frequency is the frequency of a certain allele among all alleles of the same gene in a population.
4. Phenotype frequency is the frequency of individuals with a particular phenotype in a population.
5. Hardy-Weinberg genetic equilibrium is a condition in which the allele frequencies in a population remain the same from generation to generation.

MULTIPLE CHOICE

1. b   2. c   3. b   4. d   5. a

SHORT ANSWER

1. Individuals represented by the two ends are those with extreme variations of a specific trait.
2. Variations arise through mutation, recombination during meiosis, and the random pairing of gametes during fertilization.

3. (1) No net mutations occur; (2) individuals neither enter nor leave the population; (3) the population is large; (4) individuals mate randomly; and (5) selection does not occur.
4. no, because those genes are not available for the next generation

STRUCTURES AND FUNCTIONS

Phenotype frequencies: red = $0.625 \times 0.625 = 0.391$; white = $0.375 \times 0.375 = 0.141$; pink = $1 - 0.391 - 0.141 = 0.468$. Allele frequencies: $R = 0.391 + (0.468 \div 2) = 0.625$; $r = 0.141 + (0.468 \div 2) = 0.375$.

Section 16-2

VOCABULARY REVIEW

1. Immigration is the movement of individuals into a population. Emigration is the movement of individuals out of a population.
2. Gene flow is the movement of genes from one population to another. Genetic drift is a change in allele frequencies in a population due to random events.
3. Random mating is mating that occurs without regard to genetic makeup. Assortative mating is mating based on similarity of characteristics.
4. In stabilizing selection, individuals with the average form of a trait have the highest fitness. In directional selection, individuals with one extreme form of a trait have the highest fitness.

MULTIPLE CHOICE

1. c   2. d   3. a   4. c   5. b

SHORT ANSWER

1. mutations, gene flow, genetic drift, nonrandom mating, and natural selection
2. By producing totally new alleles for a trait, mutations can change allele frequencies.
3. Matings with some degree of kinship may occur, increasing the chance of offspring with disorders caused by recessive genes.
4. The bright coloration may increase a male's chances of being selected for mating by a female.
5. Genetic homozygosity leaves no variation for natural selection to act on. Therefore, a new disease could wipe out the entire population.
6. directional selection; the cow would not eliminate all white flowers because the allele for white flowers is also carried by plants with pink flowers, which are not eaten. Crosses between plants with pink flowers would continue to produce some plants with white flowers.

STRUCTURES AND FUNCTIONS

a, disruptive; b, directional; c, stabilizing

Section 16-3

VOCABULARY REVIEW

1. Morphology is the internal and external structure and appearance of an organism.
2. Geographic isolation is the physical separation of members of a population.
3. Punctuated equilibrium is a pattern of species formation in which periods of sudden speciation are preceded and followed by long periods with little speciation.

MULTIPLE CHOICE

1. d   2. a   3. b   4. c   5. b

SHORT ANSWER

1. A satisfactory definition is not provided for species of extinct organisms or for organisms that do not reproduce sexually.
2. Individuals do not waste gametes by producing offspring that cannot reproduce.
3. Some species of moths on the Hawaiian Islands appear to have evolved during the past thousand years, whereas speciation in other organisms may take millions of years. The fossil record shows that periods of a few thousand years during which many species appeared were separated by much longer periods during which there was little speciation.
4. If the peninsulas become islands, the species that live there could become geographically isolated and eventually evolve into different species.

STRUCTURES AND FUNCTIONS

They may have other barriers to mating, such as geographic isolation, postzygotic isolation, and prezygotic isolation (they may not recognize one another's mating call).

Section 17-1
VOCABULARY REVIEW

1. Taxonomy is the science of describing, naming, and classifying organisms. A taxon is any particular group within a taxonomic system.
2. A kingdom is the largest category in Linnaeus's system of classifying life. A species is the smallest category in the system, containing only a single organism type.
3. A phylum is the largest subset within the animal kingdom of Linnaeus. A division is the largest subset within the plant kingdom.
4. A species name is the two-part scientific name of an organism. The species identifier is the second part of an organism's scientific name.
5. A species is the smallest taxonomic group, containing only a single kind of organism. Subspecies are animals that belong to the same species but live in different areas.

MULTIPLE CHOICE

1. c   2. b   3. a   4. d   5. c

SHORT ANSWER

1. Sample answers: Both systems divided all living things into two main groups, animals and plants, but Aristotle's system had three sublevels each for animals and plants, whereas Linnaeus's system had six sublevels. Aristotle also divided animals on the basis of habitat and plants on the basis of stem differences, whereas Linnaeus divided all organisms mainly on the basis of morphology. Aristotle used common names for organisms, whereas Linnaeus used binomial nomenclature.
2. Scientists use binomial nomenclature, a system in which each organism is identified with two names, the genus and the species identifier.
3. Modern taxonomists consider the evolutionary history of an organism when classifying the organism; Linnaeus considered mainly the organism's morphology.
4. Answers will vary. Aristotle's division of the animal kingdom into land, water, and air dwellers does not describe accurate morphological or evolutionary relationships among animals.

For example, bats and birds are air dwellers, and whales and fish are water dwellers, but bats are more closely related to whales than to birds, and whales are more closely related to bats than to fish.

STRUCTURES AND FUNCTIONS

a, species; b, genus; c, family; d, order; e, class; f, phylum or division; g, domain

Section 17-2
VOCABULARY REVIEW

1. Systematics is the branch of biology that organizes living things in the context of their natural relationships.
2. A phylogenetic diagram is a diagram that uses a branching pattern to indicate how closely related a subset of taxa are thought to be.
3. Cladistics is a system of phylogenetic analysis in which shared and derived characters of organisms are used to group taxa.

MULTIPLE CHOICE

1. d   2. b   3. c   4. a   5. b

SHORT ANSWER

1. Types of evidence include the morphology of fossil and living species, patterns of embryological development, and comparisons of chromosomes and macromolecules, such as DNA and RNA.
2. An out-group in cladistic analysis is a group of organisms that is only distantly related to the other organisms being analyzed. The out-group provides a starting point for the comparisons with the other organisms.
3. A derived character is found only among members of a particular group. Therefore, cladistic taxonomists assume that the character evolved within that group and that all of the organisms in the group have a common ancestor.
4. Sample answer: The fossil organism thought to be the common ancestor could have been on another branch of the phylogenetic diagram, sharing an earlier ancestor with both modern species. The changes in the protein's amino acid sequence may have been nonrandom, affected by natural selection, or produced at a greater-than-normal rate.

STRUCTURES AND FUNCTIONS

1. 3 and 4; 2. D; 3. G

Section 17-3
VOCABULARY REVIEW

1. prokaryotic, unicellular, both
2. prokaryotic, unicellular, both
3. eukaryotic, both, both
4. eukaryotic, both, heterotrophy
5. eukaryotic, multicellular, autotrophy (rarely heterotrophy)
6. eukaryotic, multicellular, heterotrophy

MULTIPLE CHOICE

1. b   2. c   3. a   4. c   5. d   6. b

SHORT ANSWER

1. Archaebacteria can flourish in harsh environments, such as sulfurous hot springs and very salty lakes, where eubacteria cannot. Also their cell membranes and biochemical and genetic properties are different from those of eubacteria.

2. Fungi include some unicellular forms, but plants do not; most plants are autotrophic, but all fungi are heterotrophic. Fungi have cell walls made of chitin, while plant cell walls are made of cellulose.

3. Multicellular heterotrophic organisms are included in kingdoms Protista, Fungi, Plantae, and Animalia.

4. Differences in rRNA sequences suggest that all organisms can be divided into three broad groups.

5. Other characteristics, such as the presence or absence of a nucleus and the type of nutrition, are more useful for understanding phylogenetic relationships. This system would place some organisms in the same group even though they are very different with regard to these characteristics.

STRUCTURES AND FUNCTIONS

a, Bacteria; b, Archaea; c, Eukarya; d–f, Protista, Plantae, Fungi

Section 18-1

VOCABULARY REVIEW

1. Ecology is the study of the interactions between organisms and the living and nonliving components of their environment.

2. Interdependence in an ecosystem occurs because all organisms interact with other organisms and the abiotic portions of the environment, and their survival depends on these interactions.

3. The biosphere is the thin volume of Earth and its atmosphere that supports life.

4. An ecosystem is a component of the biosphere that includes all of the organisms and the nonliving environment found in a particular place.

5. A community includes all interacting organisms living in an area.

6. A population is a group within a community that includes all the members of a species that live in one place at one time.

MULTIPLE CHOICE

1. b   **2.** c   **3.** d   **4.** a

SHORT ANSWER

1. When more acorns are produced by oak trees the populations of mice and deer that eat acorns increases. This causes an increase in the population of ticks that feed on these animals. The ticks carry the bacterium that causes Lyme disease, therefore human cases of the disease may also increase.

2. The applications of ecological models are limited because the models are normally very simple and do not accurately reflect the complex nature of real ecosytems.

3. A population consists of all members of a single species that live in an area, whereas a community consists of all organisms of any species that live in an area.

4. Since plants consume CO_2 during photosynthesis, extensive deforestation could result in a rise in atmospheric CO_2 levels, contributing to a change in the environment.

STRUCTURES AND FUNCTIONS

from left to right top row: 3, community; 5, organism; 1, biosphere; bottom row: 4, population; and 2, ecosystem

Section 18-2

VOCABULARY REVIEW

1. A habitat is the place where an organism lives. A resource is one of the materials or the energy an organism needs to survive.

2. A biotic factor is a living component of the environment that influences an organism. An abiotic factor is a nonliving physical or chemical characteristic of the environment that influences an organism.

3. A conformer is an organism whose internal conditions change as the environment changes. A regulator is an organism that uses energy to keep its internal conditions within an optimal range as the environment changes.

4. Dormancy is a long-term strategy to escape unfavorable environmental conditions by an organism that involves a period of reduced activity. Migration is also a strategy for escaping unfavorable conditions, but it involves organisms moving to a more favorable habitat.

5. A generalist is a species with a broad niche. A specialist is a species with a narrow niche.

MULTIPLE CHOICE

1. d   **2.** a   **3.** c   **4.** b   **5.** a

SHORT ANSWER

1. Abiotic factors include temperature, humidity, pH, salinity, O_2 concentration, amount of sunlight, availability of nitrogen, and precipitation. Temperature may influence humidity and precipitation. Precipitation may influence pH, nitrogen availability, and salinity.

2. dormancy during the period of unfavorable conditions and migration to a more favorable habitat

3. The opossum feeds on almost anything, while the koala feeds only on the leaves of a few species of eucalyptus trees.

4. The habitat is where an organism lives, but its niche is how that organism interacts in its habitat and with other organisms within the habitat.

5. Pesticides could be developed that make those limits narrower, environmental conditions could be altered (e.g., through refrigeration or desiccation) so that they lie outside those limits, or human activities could be modified to occur when or where conditions lie outside those limits.

STRUCTURES AND FUNCTIONS

a, regulator (any mammal or bird); b, conformer (any other organism)

Section 18-3

VOCABULARY REVIEW

1. A producer is an autotroph; a consumer is a heterotroph.

2. Gross primary productivity is the rate at which producers in an ecosystem capture energy. Net primary productivity is the rate at which this energy is used to produce organic material.

3. A food chain is a single pathway of feeding relationships among organisms in an ecosystem that results in energy transfer. A food web is a feeding relationship consisting of interlinked food chains.

MULTIPLE CHOICE

1. c   **2.** b   **3.** a   **4.** d   **5.** b

SHORT ANSWER

1. desert, open ocean, lake, tropical rain forest
2. Decomposers return nutrients in dead tissues and wastes to the soil or water; producers can obtain these nutrients directly.
3. Some of the organisms in a trophic level escape being eaten; some energy is stored in molecules that consumers cannot break down; some of the energy at lower levels is used for cellular respiration and is not transferred; some energy is lost as heat.
4. Because only about 10 percent of the energy at one level is transferred to the next, after a few transfers there is too little energy to support additional levels.
5. Without decomposers, the nutrients stored in the bodies and wastes of other organisms would not be available for further cycling through the ecosystem. Eventually, the soil or water would be depleted of critical nutrients and energy flow through the ecosystem would stop.

STRUCTURES AND FUNCTIONS

a, yes; b, no; c, yes; d, yes; e, yes; f, yes

Section 18-4
VOCABULARY REVIEW

1. All three are biogeochemical cycles that involve the movement of water, carbon, and nitrogen, respectively, between the living and nonliving parts of an ecosystem.
2. All three are parts of the nitrogen cycle; nitrogen fixation converts nitrogen gas into ammonia, nitrification converts ammonia into nitrites and nitrates, and denitrification converts nitrates back into nitrogen gas.

MULTIPLE CHOICE

1. b   2. a   3. d   4. c   5. b

SHORT ANSWER

1. Precipitation removes water from the atmosphere, and transpiration and evaporation return water to the atmosphere.
2. Autotrophs take CO_2 from the environment and incorporate it into organic compounds during photosynthesis; both autotrophs and heterotrophs release CO_2 from organic compounds during cellular respiration; and decomposers also release CO_2.
3. Nitrogen-fixing bacteria are found in the soil and in the roots of some kinds of plants. These bacteria convert nitrogen gas into a form which plants can absorb and use to make proteins.
4. The crop plants absorb much of the nitrogen from the soil and incorporate it into organic compounds. When the plants are harvested and removed from the field, the nitrogen leaves with them. Some of the nitrogen returns to the atmosphere through denitrification.

STRUCTURES AND FUNCTIONS

a, precipitation; b, transpiration; c, photosynthesis; d, cellular respiration; e, nitrogen fixation; f, denitrification

Section 19-1
VOCABULARY REVIEW

1. Population density is a measure of how crowded a population is, expressed as the number of individuals per unit of area or volume. Dispersion is the spatial distribution of individuals within a population, expressed as clumped, uniform, or random patterns.
2. The death rate is the number of deaths that occur in a population during a given period of time, but the life expectancy is how long, on average, an individual is expected to live.

MULTIPLE CHOICE

1. a   2. d   3. c   4. b   5. a

SHORT ANSWER

1. Individuals are clustered in a clumped distribution, separated by a fairly consistent distance in a uniform distribution, and located independent of the locations of others in a random distribution.
2. A clumped distribution can occur when animals gather into herds or flocks or when resources, such as food or nesting sites, are clumped.
3. A uniform distribution can occur when a bird or other animal claims an area and excludes other individuals in the population from that area.
4. For the first five years of life, the survivorship curve would look like a Type II or Type III curve; thereafter it would look like a Type I curve.

STRUCTURES AND FUNCTIONS

1. Z 2. X 3. Y 4. X = human or elephant, Y = bird, Z = oyster, salmon, or insect

Section 19-2
VOCABULARY REVIEW

1. Growth rate is the amount by which a population's size changes in a given time; it is equal to the birth rate minus the death rate.
2. Exponential growth is a phenomenon in which a population grows more rapidly as it becomes larger; a limiting factor in the environment ultimately restrains population growth.

MULTIPLE CHOICE

1. b   2. a   3. c   4. d   5. a

SHORT ANSWER

1. Birth rate = 4 million/265 million = 0.015; death rate = 2.4 million/265 million = 0.009; growth rate = 0.015 − 0.009 = 0.006.
2. Elton found that both hare and lynx populations underwent regular cycles, with peaks in the lynx population usually following those in the hare population by a year or two. Other evidence showed that hare populations underwent the same cycles on islands without lynxes.
3. Inbreeding can reduce the number of offspring produced, increase susceptibility to disease, decrease genetic variability, and reduce a population's ability to adapt to changing environmental conditions.
4. Population after 1 year = 01.02 × 100,000,000 = 102,000,000; after 2 years = 01.02 × 102,000,000 = 104,040,000; after 3 years = 01.02 × 104,040,000 = 106,120,800; after 4 years = 01.02 × 106,120,800 = 108,243,216; after 5 years = 01.02 × 108,243,216 = 110,408,080.

STRUCTURES AND FUNCTIONS

1. birth rate is high and death rate is low
2. birth rate equals death rate
3. carrying capacity
4. logistic model

Section 19-3

VOCABULARY REVIEW

1. The hunter-gatherer lifestyle is one in which humans obtain food by hunting animals and gathering roots, berries, nuts, shellfish, and fruits.
2. The agricultural revolution occurred about 10,000 to 12,000 years ago, when humans first domesticated animals and cultivated plants for food.
3. A developed country is a modern, industrialized country.
4. A developing country is one with a relatively low level of industrial activity and financial wealth.

MULTIPLE CHOICE

1. c   **2.** d   **3.** c   **4.** a   **5.** c

SHORT ANSWER

1. Agriculture greatly stabilized and increased the available food supply.
2. The death rate declined due to better sanitation and hygiene, control of disease, increased availability of food, and improved economic conditions.
3. Most developing countries are poor and have high population growth rates.
4. Improvements in health and hygiene in the world's poorer countries caused mortality rates to drop. This caused the world population growth rate to increase.
5. This might happen in a country that is experiencing a high rate of immigration or emigration.

STRUCTURES AND FUNCTIONS

1. A–C   2 A–B   3. D–E   4. B–C

Section 20-1

VOCABULARY REVIEW

1. A predator is an organism that captures, kills, and consumes another individual, the prey.
2. A herbivore is an animal that eats plants. Some plants defend against herbivores by producing secondary compounds that are poisonous, irritating, or bad-tasting.
3. A parasite is an organism that feeds on another organism, known as the host.

MULTIPLE CHOICE

1. a   **2.** a   **3.** d   **4.** b   **5.** a

SHORT ANSWER

1. They protect plants from herbivores by making the plants poisonous, irritating, or bad-tasting.
2. The fundamental niche is the range of conditions that the species can potentially use. The realized niche is the part of the niche that the species actually used.
3. Ectoparasites live on their host but not inside the host; endoparasites live inside the host's body.
4. When two species of finches are found living on the same island, they have different-sized beaks, allowing them to reduce competition by eating different food resources.

5. In the laboratory, the two species may be competing for the same limited resource(s). In a natural environment, the two species may avoid competition by using different resources.

STRUCTURES AND FUNCTIONS

1. endoparasite; 2. physical defense; 3. mimicry; 4. secondary compound; 5. ectoparasite; 6. pollinator

Section 20-2

VOCABULARY REVIEW

1. Species richness is the number of species in a community.
2. Primary succession is the development of a community in an area that has not supported life previously.
3. The species-area effect is a relationship in which larger areas usually contain more species than smaller areas do.

MULTIPLE CHOICE

1. a   **2.** b   **3.** a   **4.** b   **5.** b

SHORT ANSWER

1. Primary succession often proceeds very slowly because the area has not supported life previously and thus the minerals necessary for plant growth are unavailable.
2. In general, the closer a community is to the equator, the greater its species richness will be.
3. Because agricultural fields usually contain one species of crop plant, they have low community stability, and they are therefore more vulnerable to outbreaks of insect pests or disease.
4. Soil is needed for succession to take place. Winds and precipitation will remove most of the soil that forms on the slopes and carry it to the valley.

STRUCTURES AND FUNCTIONS

D,1; C, 2; B, 3; A, 4

Section 21-1

VOCABULARY REVIEW

1. A biome is a very large terrestrial ecosystem that contains a number of smaller but related ecosystems within it.
2. The tundra is a cold and largely treeless biome that forms a continuous belt across northern North America, Europe, and Asia.
3. The taiga is a biome dominated by cone-bearing evergreen trees that stretches across northern Europe, Asia, and North America.
4. A savanna is a tropical or temperate grassland with scattered trees and shrubs found in Africa, South America, and Australia.
5. A canopy is a continuous layer formed by treetops in a tropical rain forest.

MULTIPLE CHOICE

1. d   **2.** a   **3.** b   **4.** c   **5.** b

SHORT ANSWER

1. The winters are long and bitterly cold; permafrost prevents tree roots from penetrating far into the soil; there is very little precipitation; the growing season is very short.
2. The actively growing part of the plant is at or below the ground, not at the tip of the stem.

3. Some trees of the savanna conserve water during the dry season by shedding their leaves; the above-ground parts of grasses often die during the dry season and regenerate after a period of rain.
4. Plants may open their stomata only at night, have sharp protective spines, and have a waxy coating on their leaves to reduce evaporation.
5. The taiga has a shorter growing season, less precipitation, and poorer soil than do temperate deciduous forests. These characteristics make the taiga less suitable for growing many crops.
6. As they grow, vines cling to other objects. This adaptation enables vines to reach higher levels in the rain forest, where there is more light.

STRUCTURES AND FUNCTIONS
a, tropical forest; b, tundra; c, temperate grassland; d, desert

Section 21-2
VOCABULARY REVIEW
1. The photic zone is the part of the ocean that receives sunlight. The aphotic zone is the deeper part of the ocean where sunlight cannot penetrate.
2. The neritic zone extends from the end of the intertidal zone over the continental shelf. The oceanic zone is the part of the ocean that extends beyond the continental shelf.
3. The pelagic zone is the open ocean. The benthic zone is the ocean bottom.
4. A eutrophic lake is rich in organic matter and vegetation. An oligotrophic lake contains little organic matter.

MULTIPLE CHOICE
1. c   2. a   3. b   4. c   5. d

SHORT ANSWER
1. Crabs burrow into the sand or mud; clams, mussels, and oysters retreat into their shells; sea anemones and sea stars cling to surfaces with a muscular disk or tube feet, respectively.
2. Plankton is consumed by many larger organisms, forming the base of many marine food chains.
3. The oceanic zone covers a vast area; thus, even though productivity per square meter is low, total productivity is high.
4. Producers near deep-sea vents obtain energy from hydrogen sulfide through chemosynthesis.
5. The nutrients would stimulate the growth of photosynthetic organisms, which would increase the concentration of organic matter in the lake, making the lake's water murky. If the situation persisted, the organic matter would accumulate and the lake would eventually fill in and disappear.

STRUCTURES AND FUNCTIONS
a, oceanic zone; b, pelagic zone; c, benthic zone; d, photic zone; e, aphotic zone; f, neritic zone; g, intertidal zone

Section 22-1
VOCABULARY REVIEW
1. the variety of organisms in a given area
2. Species evenness is a measure of biodiversity that considers how many individuals belong to each species in a community.

3. Genetic diversity is the amount of genetic variation among the individuals in a population.

MULTIPLE CHOICE
1. b   2. d   3. a   4. c   5. b

SHORT ANSWER
1. The geosphere is Earth's rocky interior from the solid crustal surface to the center of the planet. The hydrosphere is the portion of Earth that is water, and the atmosphere is the gaseous envelope that surrounds Earth. The biosphere is the part of Earth where life exists.
2. A population with a low genetic diversity could be more likely to be wiped out by a disease because the population has less genetic variation and therefore less chance of surviving the natural selection caused by the disease.
3. The greenhouse effect is a phenomenon in which atmospheric gases such as CO_2 trap reradiated heat from the Earth, much as the glass panes of a greenhouse retain heat within the greenhouse.
4. This type of storage preserves seeds so that the plants can be grown and tested in the future for their potential value, even if the natural habitats of the plants are destroyed.

STRUCTURES AND FUNCTIONS
1. C   2. B   3. A   4. B   5. C   6. B

Section 22-2
VOCABULARY REVIEW
1. Smog is air pollution which consists of water vapor mixed with chemicals.
2. Extinction is the death of all members of a species.
3. Keystone species are species that are critical to the functioning of an ecosystem.
4. A CFC is a chemical once widely used as a coolant and aerosol propellant that catalyzes the breakdown of ozone in the upper atmosphere.

MULTIPLE CHOICE
1. b   2. b   3. d   4. b   5. c

SHORT ANSWER
1. Acid precipitation is the result of air pollutants that combine with water vapor in the atmosphere to form acids, causing precipitation that is more acidic than normal.
2. increased CO_2 in the atmosphere and global warming; increased use of resources to produce homes, schools, roads, and hospitals; decrease of fresh water availability; and an increase in wastes
3. Sustainability is the ability to meet human needs in a way that will allow a human population to survive indefinitely.
4. A controlled experiment in which all other variables are held constant would be needed. A reduction in global CO_2 levels followed by a decrease in global temperatures would support the idea of cause-and-effect relationship.

STRUCTURES AND FUNCTIONS
a, use of chlorofluorocarbons; b, increased amounts of ultraviolet radiation reach the Earth's surface; c, increased incidence of skin cancer in humans; d, increased levels of atmospheric CO_2; e and f, changes in rainfall patterns, changes in soil moisture, changes in sea level, shifting of agricultural regions, disruption of natural ecosystems

Section 22-3

VOCABULARY REVIEW

1. Conservation biology is a discipline that seeks to identify and maintain natural areas that retain a high biodiversity.
2. Restoration biology is a discipline that seeks to reverse major environmental damage and replace missing ecosystem components.

MULTIPLE CHOICE

1. b   **2.** c   **3.** a   **4.** b   **5.** c

SHORT ANSWER

1. A biodiversity hotspot is an area that contains an especially high density of unique but threatened or endangered species.
2. The winter and summer destinations of most migratory birds are not in the same country.
3. Ecotourism is tourism involving people who want to see intact ecosystems and their unique organisms. Income generated from ecotourism increases the value of natural ecosystems, thus providing an incentive for preserving biodiversity.
4. Actions include the drainage of land and the planting of melalenca trees.
5. Answer will vary, but could include that restoring the Everglades will protect endangered species, such as the Florida panther, and restore the water flow needed by many organisms. The restoration will also protect groundwater resources needed by people, reduce invasive plant species, and restore the breeding grounds and the nurseries of many species.

STRUCTURES AND FUNCTIONS

a, wildlife refuges; b, migratory birds; c, the whooping crane; d, answers may vary and include careful study of the species to be reintroduced, regulation of hunting, and establishment of refuges; e, the Everglades; f, answers may vary and include eliminating some drainage canals, restoring the Kissimmee River to its original channel, cutting back stands of melaleuca trees, and purchasing lands for park protection

Section 23-1

VOCABULARY REVIEW

1. A halophile lives in very high salt concentrations, and a thermoacidophile lives in extremely acidic, hot environments.
2. A bacillus is rod-shaped, a coccus is spherical, and a spirillum is spiral.
3. A streptococcus is a coccus that occurs in chains; a staphylococcus is a coccus that occurs in grapelike clusters.
4. A Gram-positive bacterium retains the Gram stain and appears purple; a Gram-negative bacterium does not retain the Gram stain and takes up a second pink stain.

MULTIPLE CHOICE

1. c   **2.** b   **3.** d   **4.** c   **5.** d

SHORT ANSWER

1. Bacteria with large amounts of peptidoglycan in the cell wall are able to retain the Gram stain, while those with less peptidoglycan do not.
2. They convert atmospheric nitrogen to ammonia, which plants can use.

3. Cyanobacteria produce much of Earth's oxygen; some species fix atmospheric nitrogen.
4. Some bacteria cause disease; others make vitamin K and help in digestion.
5. Aerobic organisms require the presence of oxygen, which was first generated by cyanobacteria as a waste product of photosynthesis.
6. These explorations revealed the existence of archaea. Because some archaeal genes resemble bacterial genes while other archaeal genes resemble eukaryotic genes, some biologists think that archaea may resemble ancestral eukaryotes.

STRUCTURES AND FUNCTIONS

1. bacillus 2. coccus 3. spirillum 4. streptococcus

Section 23-2

VOCABULARY REVIEW

1. A capsule is an outer covering of polysaccharides made by many bacteria; an endospore is a dormant structure consisting of a thick outer covering that surrounds a bacterial cell's DNA.
2. A pilus is a short, hairlike protein structure that extends from the cell surface of some bacteria; conjugation is a process during which DNA is transferred from one cell to another through a pilus.
3. An obligate anaerobe cannot survive in the presence of oxygen; a facultative anaerobe can live with or without oxygen.
4. Transformation is a process by which bacteria obtain DNA from its external environment; transduction is the transfer of DNA from one bacterium to another by a virus.

MULTIPLE CHOICE

1. c   **2.** b   **3.** a   **4.** c   **5.** a

SHORT ANSWER

1. Photosynthesis takes place in internal foldings of the cell membrane called thylakoids.
2. A glycocalyx is a fuzzy coating of sticky sugars that makes up the capsule of some bacteria. It enables bacteria to attach to the surface of host cells and tissues.
3. oxygen, temperature, pH
4. Transduction involves DNA transfer by viruses.
5. New cells are not produced, and the number of cells does not increase.

STRUCTURES AND FUNCTIONS

1. assists the cell in attaching to other surfaces and in genetic recombination
2. protects the cell and assists it in attaching to other surfaces
3. protects the cell and gives it shape
4. regulates the movement of materials into and out of the cell and contains important enzymes
5. carries genetic information
6. carries genes obtained through genetic recombination
7. moves the cell

Section 23-3

VOCABULARY REVIEW

1. Pathology is the scientific study of disease.
2. An exotoxin is a poison that is secreted into the environment by Gram-positive bacteria.

3. An endotoxin is a poison that is associated with the outer membrane of Gram-negative bacteria.
4. Zoonosis is a disease that can pass from animals to humans.
5. Bioremediation is the process of harnessing bacteria to recycle compounds.

MULTIPLE CHOICE

1. d   2. c   3. b   4. c   5. d

SHORT ANSWER

1. sneezes, coughs, direct contact, and sexual contact
2. Diseases affecting nerves include botulism and tetanus; diseases affecting the intestine include salmonella food poisoning and cholera; and diseases affecting the skin include anthrax, Lyme disease, and staph infections.
3. inhibition of cell-wall synthesis and protein synthesis
4. Foods include buttermilk, sour cream, yogurt, ricotta and cheddar cheese, sauerkraut, and pickles.
5. Since broad-spectrum antibiotics affect a wide variety of organisms, they are likely to be more effective than specific antibiotics when the identity of the pathogen is unknown. If overused, however, they may cause several types of bacteria to develop resistance.

STRUCTURES AND FUNCTIONS

A. The bacteria are insensitive to A because bacterial growth around disk A is uninhibited.
B. The bacteria are moderately sensitive to B because some growth inhibition is occurring around disk B.
C. The bacteria are insensitive to C because bacterial growth around disk C is uninhibited.
D. The bacteria are very sensitive to D because of the relatively larger area of growth inhibition around disk D.

Section 24-1

VOCABULARY REVIEW

1. A virus is a nonliving particle composed of a nucleic acid and a protein or lipoprotein coat.
2. A capsid is the protein coat that surrounds the nucleic acid in a virus.
3. A retrovirus is a virus that contains RNA and the enzyme reverse transcriptase.
4. In the lytic cycle, a virus invades a host cell, produces new viruses, and kills the host cell, which releases the new viruses.
5. In the lysogenic cycle, a virus remains within a host cell for an extended period of time.

MULTIPLE CHOICE

1. d   2. c   3. d   4. a   5. c

SHORT ANSWER

1. Stanley was able to crystallize the tobacco mosaic virus, which suggested that viruses were chemicals rather than tiny cells.
2. radiation and certain chemicals
3. An RNA virus releases its RNA into the host cell, and that RNA is transcribed into DNA by reverse transcriptase; the DNA is then integrated into the host cell's genome.
4. The influenza virus mutates quickly, producing new strains. The flu vaccine targets a different strain each year.

5. Bacteriophages are very effective at injecting foreign DNA into bacteria. Genetic engineers can use bacteriophages to introduce DNA of interest to humans into bacteria.

STRUCTURES AND FUNCTIONS

c, the virus attaches to the host cell's surface; a, the viral DNA is injected into the host cell; e, the viral DNA replicates and directs the synthesis of viral proteins; d, new virus particles are assembled; b, the host cell ruptures, releasing the new virus particles.

Section 24-2

VOCABULARY REVIEW

1. An inactivated virus is used to make a vaccine because it is not able to replicate in a host.
2. An attenuated virus is a weakened form of a virus that is used to make a vaccine because it cannot cause disease.
3. An oncogene is a gene that causes cancer by blocking the normal controls on cell reproduction.
4. A proto-oncogene is a gene that usually controls cell growth and can be converted to an oncogene, causing cancer.
5. an antiviral agent that interferes with the synthesis of capsids during viral replication

MULTIPLE CHOICE

1. a   2. d   3. b   4. c   5. a

SHORT ANSWER

1. rabies, smallpox, HIV, hantavirus, and Ebola virus
2. Some chickenpox viral particles persist in nerve cells; later in life, the particles travel along nerve fibers to the skin, where they cause shingles.
3. antiviral drugs, and control of animal vectors that spread viral diseases
4. Certain viruses can cause normal genes to mutate into oncogenes.
5. If individuals from a community venture into a previously undeveloped forest, they may encounter an animal that harbors a previously unknown virus. If these individuals become infected, they can carry this infection to their community.
6. Such a drug would block transcription of host genes as well as viral genes.

STRUCTURES AND FUNCTIONS

a, glycoprotein; b, RNA genome; c, reverse transcriptase; d, envelope; e, capsid

Section 25-1

VOCABULARY REVIEW

1. A protist is a single-celled or simple multicellular eukaryotic organism.
2. Binary fission is a method of asexual reproduction in which a single cell divides into two identical cells.
3. Multiple fission is a form of cell division that produces more than two offspring.
4. Conjugation is a method of sexual reproduction in which two individuals join and exchange genetic material.

MULTIPLE CHOICE

1. d   2. b   3. c   4. c   5. c

SHORT ANSWER

1. Protists obtain energy by photosynthesis (autotrophy) or by eating other organisms (heterotrophy). In autotrophy, protists make their own food molecules by absorbing the energy from sunlight with the help of specialized pigments. In heterotrophy, protists get energy by engulfing and eating small organisms or by secreting enzymes into the environment and then absorbing the small molecules that are formed.
2. Protists are classified by reproduction, method of obtaining energy, or type of movement.
3. In endosymbiosis, an organism lives inside a larger organism. Over time, the smaller organism becomes an organelle.
4. Since protists are eukaryotes, their chromosomes are contained inside a nucleus, which must break down and then reform for conjugation to occur. Bacteria lack a nucleus, so division and exchange of genetic material is simpler.

STRUCTURES AND FUNCTIONS

a. sexual reproduction
b. asexual reproduction

Section 25-2

VOCABULARY REVIEW

1. Cilia are short hairlike cytoplasmic projections that beat in waves. Flagella are long, whiplike structures made of microtubules.
2. Both are openings on the surface of a paramecium. Food enters the gullet through the mouth pore, and undigested food molecules are expelled through the anal pore.
3. Both contain DNA. The macronucleus is large, contains multiple copies of DNA, and is responsible for metabolic functions, and the micronucleus is small and participates in the exchange of genetic material during conjugation.

MULTIPLE CHOICE

1. b   2. b   3. c   4. c   5. c

SHORT ANSWER

1. The hard tests that cover the bodies of these organisms sink to the bottom of the ocean, where they accumulate as layers of sediment.
2. Cilia lining the oral groove sweep food down the groove to the mouth pore, which opens into the gullet. Food passes from the gullet into food vacuoles, where digestion occurs. Undigested molecules are expelled via the anal pore.
3. A pseudopodium extends forward as cytoplasm streams into it, and the organism moves forward. A food particle is surrounded by pseudopodia and engulfed.
4. The protozoans use the circulatory system of their human and mosquito hosts to transport them through their hosts' bodies, and they depend on the mosquitoes to transport them from one human host to another.

STRUCTURES AND FUNCTIONS

a, anal pore; b, gullet; c, cilia; d, oral groove; e, food vacuole; f, pellicle; g, contractile vacuole

Section 25-3

VOCABULARY REVIEW

1. A fruiting body is a stationary, reproductive, sporebearing structure of funguslike protists.
2. A gametangium is a single-celled chamber in which the gametes of algae are produced.
3. A euglenoid is a flagellated, unicellular alga that has both plantlike and animal-like features.
4. An accessory pigment is a pigment that captures light energy and transfers it to chlorophyll *a*.

MULTIPLE CHOICE

1. b   2. d   3. c   4. d   5. c

SHORT ANSWER

1. Algae lack tissue differentiation and have no true roots, stems, and leaves. The gametangia of algae are single-celled; the gametangia of plants are multicelled.
2. Photoplankton form the base of nearly all marine and freshwater food chains.
3. Algae can exist as unicellular, colonial, filamentous, and multicellular organisms.
4. Dinoflagellates have two flagella of unequal length that are oriented perpendicular to each other. Dinoflagellates also have cell walls made of cellulose plates that look like armor.
5. plantlike: presence of chlorophyll, ability to photosynthesize; animal-like: lack cell walls, are highly motile
6. Brown and red algae are multicellular, like plants. They contain structures that resemble the structures of plants, although the structures lack tissue differentiation.

STRUCTURES AND FUNCTIONS

a. Myxomycota
b. Chytridiomycota
c. Dictyostelida
d. Oomycota

Section 25-4

VOCABULARY REVIEW

1. A sporozoite is the *Plasmodium* stage that enters the human bloodstream and infects the liver. A merozoite is the stage that emerges from the liver and infects red blood cells.
2. Giardiasis is the intestinal illness caused by *Giardia*. Trichomoniasis is the sexually transmitted illness caused by *Trichomonas*.
3. Alginate is a commercially important polysaccharide derived from the cell walls of brown algae. Agar is an important polysaccharide that comes from red algae.

MULTIPLE CHOICE

1. c   2. d   3. a   4. a   5. c

SHORT ANSWER

1. Protists live in a close relationship with corals, giving the corals their color and supplying much of their carbon. Lichens are symbiotic relationships between algae and fungi. Lichens create new soil from rock. Protists live in termite guts and digest cellulose.
2. Carrageenan is added to control the texture of food products.

3. Chemotaxis in slime molds is the ability to crawl toward AMP. Human leukocytes also exhibit chemotaxis. By studying slime molds, scientists hope to better understand how leukocytes protect against disease.
4. The toxins from dinoflagellates concentrate as they move up the food chain. Clams and oysters eat the algae, and humans eat the shellfish.

STRUCTURES AND FUNCTIONS

a. sporozoites; b. sporozoites; c. liver; d. merozoites; e. red blood cells; f. gametocytes

Section 26-1
VOCABULARY REVIEW

1. A hypha is a fungal filament.
2. A mycelium is a mat of hyphae visible to the unaided eye.
3. A coenocyte is a species that has hyphae lacking septa.
4. A sporangiophore is a specialized hypha that looks like an upright stalk and bears a spore-forming sac.
5. A conidium is a fungal spore that is formed without the protection of an enclosing sac.
6. Budding is an asexual process in which part of a yeast cell pinches itself off to produce a small offspring cell.

MULTIPLE CHOICE

1. c   2. b   3. a   4. d   5. a

SHORT ANSWER

1. The cell walls of fungi contain chitin, while the cell walls of plants contain cellulose.
2. The fungus *Histoplasma capsulatum* normally grows as a mycelium in soil, but when it invades a human, it grows unicellularly as a yeast.
3. A septate hypha dries and shatters, releasing individual cells that act as spores.
4. *Plus* and *minus* refer to different mating types of hyphae that may fuse with each other during sexual reproduction.
5. Like animals, fungi store energy in the form of glycogen.
6. Because most fungi are saprophytic, they use the resources from dead organisms and make them available to other organisms in an ecosystem.
7. Most fungi consist of cells that are relatively unspecialized. Like unicellular protists, the cells of a fungus resemble each other and obtain their own nutrients directly from the environment.

STRUCTURES AND FUNCTIONS

a, septum; b, nuclei; c, cell wall; d, septate hyphae; e, coenocytic hyphae

Section 26-2
VOCABULARY REVIEW

1. A rhizoid is a zygomycete hypha that penetrates the surface on which the fungus is growing; a stolon is a zygomycete hypha that grows across the surface of the area where the zygomycete is growing.
2. A basidium is a reproductive structure produced by a basidiomycete; a basidiocarp is the above-ground spore-bearing portion of a basidiomycete.
3. An ascogonium is a female gametangium; an antheridium is a male gametangium.

4. An ascocarp is a cuplike reproductive structure produced by an ascomycete; an ascus is a spore-bearing sac that develops in an ascocarp.
5. A lichen is a symbiotic relationship between a fungus and a photosynthetic organism; a mycorrhiza is a symbiotic structure formed by a fungus and plant roots.

MULTIPLE CHOICE

1. a   2. d   3. c   4. b   5. c

SHORT ANSWER

1. In basidiomycetes, those structures consist of a stalk and a flattened cap with rows of gills on the underside; in ascomycetes, they usually resemble a cup.
2. Fungi imperfecti lack a sexual stage.
3. A mycorrhiza is a symbiotic association between a fungus and plant roots; a lichen is a symbiotic association between a fungus and usually a cyanobacterium or a green alga.
4. Lichens produce acids that decompose rocks, contributing to the production of soil.
5. Mushrooms are produced by basidiomycetes and are formed as a result of sexual reproduction. Deuteromycetes do not have a sexual stage; therefore mushrooms cannot be deuteromycetes.
6. A growing plant would benefit more from a mycorrhiza. Although a lichen contributes to the production of soil, it may take years to produce enough soil for a plant to begin to develop; a mycorrhizal fungus, on the other hand, can begin to contribute to a plant's well-being immediately.
7. The sexual reproductive structures are more specialized and distinctive than the nonreproductive or asexual reproductive structures.

STRUCTURES AND FUNCTIONS

a, sporangium; b, sporangiospores; c, rhizoid; d, gametangia; e, zygosporangium; f, meiosis

Section 26-3
VOCABULARY REVIEW

1. Aflatoxins are poisons produced by some fungi.
2. Aflatoxins cause liver cancer.
3. They may be found in peanuts, tree nuts, cottonseed, and grains, such as corn.
4. A wheat rust is a basidiomycete that attacks wheat grains.

MULTIPLE CHOICE

1. d   2. b   3. a   4. d   5. c   6. b   7. c

SHORT ANSWER

1. pregnancy, illness, and the use of some antibiotics
2. penicillin, cephalosporin, cortisone, and the hepatitis B vaccine
3. cheese, beer, wine, miso, soy sauce, tempeh, tofu, yeast, bread, and mushrooms
4. Plasmids are used to insert foreign genes into *Saccharomyces*. The yeast then uses those genes to produce foreign proteins.
5. Such substances might encourage animals to consume the reproductive structures. In doing so, the animals would help disperse the fungal spores to new locations.

STRUCTURES AND FUNCTIONS

a–c may vary and include bread, cheese, soy products, beer, and wine; *d–f* may vary and include antibiotics, cortisone, vaccines, and ethanol; *g–i*, infection, poisoning, and allergies

Section 27-1

VOCABULARY REVIEW

1. Botany is the study of plants; agriculture is the practice of growing plants or raising animals for human use.
2. A cereal is a grass that contains grains; a root crop is a plant whose roots or underground stems are rich in carbohydrates and used by humans for food.
3. A legume is a member of the pea family that bears protein-rich seeds in pods; a nut is a dry, hard fruit that does not split open.
4. A fruit is a part of a flowering plant that usually contains seeds; a vegetable is a food derived from the leaves, stems, seeds, or roots of nonwoody plants.

MULTIPLE CHOICE

1. b   2. a   3. d   4. c   5. b

SHORT ANSWER

1. A cultivar is a cultivated variety of a plant that can be distinguished from other members of its species. Examples include Thompson Seedless grapes, McIntosh apples, Valencia oranges.
2. Such diets are usually low in some amino acids. People can also eat legumes or animal protein.
3. Grains can be fermented into alcohol, which can be mixed with gasoline to make gasohol.
4. Many cereals thrive in temperate climates but do not grow well in the tropics. Rice is an exception. Many people in dry tropical areas therefore rely more on root crops.

STRUCTURES AND FUNCTIONS

cantaloupe, fruit; rice, cereal; celery, vegetable; nutmeg, spice; pecan, nut; potato, root crop; lima bean, legume; oregano, herb

Section 27-2

VOCABULARY REVIEW

1. Plant ecology is the study of the interactions between plants and the environment.
2. A weed is an undesirable plant that may crowd out crop plants or native plant species.
3. Hay fever is an allergic reaction that may be caused by pollen and results in sneezing, a runny nose, and watery eyes.

MULTIPLE CHOICE

1. c   2. a   3. b   4. d   5. a   6. d

SHORT ANSWER

1. Through photosynthesis, plants convert carbon dioxide and water into organic compounds and oxygen. Organisms that perform aerobic respiration (including plants) convert these compounds and oxygen back into carbon dioxide and water.
2. Plant roots bind soil particles together; leaves reduce erosion due to wind and rain; and dead plant parts add organic matter to the soil.
3. chestnut blight, an introduced fungal disease
4. small, drab flowers that are wind-pollinated
5. Herbivores or pathogenic microbes that keep native plants in check may not attack introduced plants. Without such natural controls, introduced plants can outcompete native plants for resources.

STRUCTURES AND FUNCTIONS

a, consumers; b, death; c, decomposers; d, nutrients
1. producers 2. nitrogen, phosphorus, potassium, iron, and magnesium

Section 28-1

VOCABULARY REVIEW

1. The sporophyte is the first phase of a plant's life cycle and is a diploid plant that produces spores; the second phase is a haploid gametophyte plant that produces eggs and sperm.
2. A spore contains a haploid reproductive cell surrounded by a hard outer wall; a seed is a plant embryo surrounded by a protective coat.
3. Both are types of plant vascular tissue; xylem carries water and inorganic nutrients from the roots to the stems and leaves, while phloem carries organic and some inorganic compounds in any direction.
4. A vascular plant has vascular tissue and true roots, stems, and leaves; a nonvascular plant has none of these.
5. An angiosperm's seeds are enclosed in fruits, while a gymnosperm's seeds are not.

MULTIPLE CHOICE

1. d   2. b   3. a   4. c   5. b

SHORT ANSWER

1. The cuticle prevents water loss from the plant; spores and/or seeds help disperse species and prevent reproductive cells from drying out; vascular tissue transports water and dissolved substances within the plant.
2. Both have chlorophylls *a* and *b*, both store energy as starch, and both have cell walls made of cellulose.
3. Spores, gametophytes, and gametes are haploid.
4. The spores of algae are motile while those of land plants are not. The spores of land plants have a protective covering while those of algae do not.

STRUCTURES AND FUNCTIONS

a, flowers, fruits; b, seeds; c, hardened vascular tissue; d, reproduction by spores

Section 28-2

VOCABULARY REVIEW

1. A bryophyte is any member of the three phyla of nonvascular plants.
2. unusual-looking plants that grow in moist, shady areas and are from the phylum Hepatophyta
3. Plants from the phylum Anthocerophyta which grow in moist, shaded areas and have long, thin, hornlike sporophytes

MULTIPLE CHOICE

1. b   2. a   3. c   4. d   5. b

SHORT ANSWER

1. The gametophyte phase is dominant.
2. The sperm must swim through water to reach an egg during sexual reproduction.
3. It is used as fuel; added to potting and gardening soils to increase their ability to retain water; and used to pack bulbs and flowers for shipping.
4. Each of their cells contains a single large chloroplast rather than numerous small ones.

5. Mosses are often one of the first species in a disturbed area, and they benefit other plants by accumulating organic and inorganic matter that begins to form a soil layer in which other plants can grow. They also prevent soil erosion.
6. One would expect to find thalloid liverworts in dryer environments since the thalloid form allows the entire body of the liverwort to be in contact with water on the surface that the plant grows on.

STRUCTURES AND FUNCTIONS

a, sporophyte; b, gametophyte; c, rhizoid

Section 28-3
VOCABULARY REVIEW

1. Both are fern leaves; a fiddlehead is a tightly coiled new leaf, and a frond is an uncoiled mature leaf.
2. Both are flowering plants; a monocot usually has one cotyledon, and a dicot usually has two. Monocots also have parallel venation in their leaves, their stems have scattered vascular bundles, and their flowers usually occur in threes. Dicots also have net venation in their leaves, their stems have radially arranged vascular bundles, and their flower parts usually occur in fours or fives.
3. Both are patterns of veins in leaves; the veins run roughly parallel to each other in parallel venation and form an interconnected network in net venation.

MULTIPLE CHOICE

1. c   2. d   3. a   4. b   5. d

SHORT ANSWER

1. Vascular plants have conducting tissues that transport water and dissolved substances within the plant; nonvascular plants do not. The strong stems of vascular plants allow the plants to grow taller than nonvascular plants, enabling them to receive more sunlight than shorter plants do.
2. Cycadophyta: have thick trunks with fernlike leaves, are male or female, and have large cones. Ginkgophyta: have tall trunks, deciduous fan-shaped leaves, and large seeds. Coniferophyta: have tall trunks, needle or scalelike leaves, and cones.
3. Angiosperms have flowers, which produce pollen, eggs, or both; seeds are enclosed in an ovary that ripens into a fruit. Gymnosperms have cones that produce either pollen or eggs; egg-producing cones hold the seeds without enclosing them.
4. Ferns were able to develop adaptations to a wider range of environments than were the other groups of nonvascular plants.

STRUCTURES AND FUNCTIONS

a, Ginkgophyta; b, Psilophyta; c, Cycadophyta; d, Coniferophyta

Section 29-1
VOCABULARY REVIEW

1. Parenchyma cells are loosely packed, cube-shaped, or elongated cells with a large central vacuole and thin cell walls; collenchyma cells are thicker and have irregularly shaped, thick cell walls; sclerenchyma cells have thick, even, rigid cell walls.

2. The dermal tissue system forms the outside covering of plants; the ground tissue system lies inside the dermal tissue and functions in storage and support; the vascular tissue system lies inside the ground tissue and functions in transport and support.
3. Apical meristems are located at the tips of stems and roots, intercalary meristems are located above the bases of leaves and stems, and lateral meristems are located near the outside of stems and roots.

MULTIPLE CHOICE

1. c   2. a   3. d   4. b   5. b

SHORT ANSWER

1. Epidermal cells are found in the nonwoody parts; their functions include gas exchange, water absorption, and water-loss prevention.
2. They are thick and have irregularly shaped cell walls; provide support; they are found in regions of the plant that are still lengthening.
3. where growth is no longer occurring; in vascular tissue, hard seed coats, and cactus spines
4. Monocots have apical meristems at the tips of stems and roots, and some have intercalary meristems above the bases of leaves and stems. Dicots have apical meristems at the tips of stems and roots, and most have lateral meristems near the outside of stems and roots.
5. The absence of cellular contents inside the walls of the water-transporting cells allows large amounts of water to move rapidly through the xylem.

STRUCTURES AND FUNCTIONS

a, companion cell; b, pit; c, sieve pore; d, sieve plate; e, tracheid; f, sieve tube member; g, vessel element

Section 29-2
VOCABULARY REVIEW

1. An adventitious root is a specialized root that grows from a stem or leaf.
2. The cortex is the portion of a primary root that lies between the epidermis and the vascular tissues.
3. The pericycle is the outermost layer or layers of the central vascular tissues in a root.
4. A macronutrient is an element that is required in relatively large amounts by a plant.
5. A micronutrient is an element that is required in relatively small amounts by a plant.

MULTIPLE CHOICE

1. d   2. a   3. b   4. c   5. a

SHORT ANSWER

1. vascular tissue
2. Pericycle cells divide to form lateral roots.
3. between primary xylem and primary phloem
4. The vascular cambium produces secondary xylem toward the inside of the root and secondary phloem toward the outside.
5. Macronutrients include nitrogen, phosphorus, potassium, calcium, magnesium, and sulfur.
6. Water absorption should be greater in parts of roots that have not undergone secondary growth. Roots with secondary growth are surrounded by cork cells, which do not absorb much water.

STRUCTURES AND FUNCTIONS

a, epidermis; b, cortex; c, pith; d, xylem; e, phloem; f, endodermis; g, dicot; h, monocot

Section 29-3

VOCABULARY REVIEW

1. Heartwood is the darker, older wood in the center of a tree that no longer transports water; sapwood is the functional, often lighter-colored wood nearer the outside of the trunk.
2. Springwood is xylem tissue composed of wide, thin-walled cells formed when water is plentiful; summerwood is xylem tissue composed of small, thick-walled cells formed when water is more limited.
3. A source is a place in a plant where carbohydrates are made or have been stored; a sink is a place in a plant where carbohydrates are stored or used.
4. Translocation is the movement of carbohydrates through a plant; transpiration is the evaporation of water from a plant.
5. The pith is formed during primary growth; wood is secondary xylem.

MULTIPLE CHOICE

1. b   2. d   3. c   4. a   5. c

SHORT ANSWER

1. The bud scales are analogous to the root cap. The bud scales are present only when the stem is not growing, whereas the root cap is always on the root.
2. The evaporation of water from a leaf puts the column of water in the xylem under tension. The column does not break because of cohesion. The column does not pull away from the xylem walls because of adhesion. Thus, water is pulled toward the leaf.
3. Wood provides structural support allowing plants to grow tall and enabling them to capture more light.

STRUCTURES AND FUNCTIONS

a, phloem; b, source; c, sink; d, xylem; e, carbohydrate (or sugar); f, water; g, carbohydrate (or sugar) and water; h, carbohydrate (or sugar); i, water

Section 29-4

VOCABULARY REVIEW

1. A petiole is a stalklike structure that attaches a leaf to a stem.
2. Mesophyll is a ground tissue composed of chloroplast-rich parenchyma cells, which is where photosynthesis takes place.
3. A guard cell is a modified cell found on the leaf epidermis that regulates gas and water exchange.

MULTIPLE CHOICE

1. b   2. d   3. a   4. c   5. a

SHORT ANSWER

1. Tendrils enable vines to climb, food traps collect small animals as a source of nutrients, and spines protect the plant from being eaten.
2. Epidermal hairs usually protect the leaf from insects and intense light.
3. The products of photosynthesis may be used as an energy source or as building blocks, either in the leaf or in other parts of the plant.
4. Epidermal cells pump potassium ions into guard cells, and water moves into the guard cells by osmo-

sis. The influx of water makes the guard cells swell, causing them to bow apart and open the stomata.
5. It would block the transport of mineral nutrients from the roots to the rest of the plant.

STRUCTURES AND FUNCTIONS

a, cuticle; b, upper epidermis; c, palisade mesophyll; d, vascular bundle; e, spongy mesophyll; f, lower epidermis

Section 30-1

VOCABULARY REVIEW

1. An antheridium produces many sperm, and an archegonium produces a single egg.
2. Homospory is the production of one type of spore. Heterospory is the production of different types of spores.
3. The integument is a thick layer of cells that surrounds a megasporangium. A micropyle is a small opening in the integument.

MULTIPLE CHOICE

1. c   2. a   3. d   4. b   5. c

SHORT ANSWER

1. Haploid: spore, archegonium, antheridium, gametophyte. Diploid: sporophyte, zygote. The gametophyte is the dominant phase.
2. The sperm of conifers are not flagellated, whereas the sperm of mosses and ferns are. The spores of conifers are of two types, whereas the spores of mosses and most ferns are of one type; also, the spores of conifers never leave the parent plant, whereas the spores of mosses and ferns do.
3. Meiosis produces spores. Mitosis produces gametes.
4. They have flagellated sperm, which must swim through water to reach and fertilize the eggs.

STRUCTURES AND FUNCTIONS

a, sori; b, sporangium; c, spores; d, gametophyte; e, antheridium; f, archegonium; g, zygote; h, sporophyte

Section 30-2

VOCABULARY REVIEW

1. An anther is a male reproductive structure that contains microsporangia. A filament is a stalklike structure that supports an anther.
2. A stigma is a female reproductive structure that traps pollen grains in a flowering plant. A style is a stalklike structure that ends in a stigma.
3. Polar nuclei are produced during the formation of an embryo sac in a flowering plant. In double fertilization, the polar nuclei fuse with one sperm nucleus while the egg fuses with another sperm.

MULTIPLE CHOICE

1. c   2. a   3. b   4. d   5. b

SHORT ANSWER

1. Three of the megaspores degenerate, and the fourth forms the structures of the embryo sac. Each of the microspores forms a pollen grain.
2. Both gymnosperms and angiosperms: wind pollination, pollen grain, pollen tube. Only in angiosperms: animal pollination, fertilization quickly following pollination, double fertilization, embryo sac, endosperm.

3. Nectar increases a plant's chances of sexual reproduction since it attracts pollinators.
4. Endosperm provides nourishment for the embryo.
5. Such plants are more likely to have fragrant flowers. Most moths and bats are nocturnal, and at night it would be easier to find flowers by smell than by sight.

STRUCTURES AND FUNCTIONS

a, filament; b, anther; c, stigma; d, style; e, ovary; f, receptacle; g, ovule; h, sepal; i, petal

Section 30-3
VOCABULARY REVIEW

1. A radicle is an embryonic root in a seed.
2. A hypocotyl is the portion of the embryonic stem between the attachment point of the cotyledons and the radicle.
3. An epicotyl is the portion of the embryonic stem above the attachment point of the cotyledons.
4. A plumule is the shoot tip and any embryonic leaves attached to its tip.
5. A hilum is a scar on a seed that marks where the seed was attached to the ovary wall.

MULTIPLE CHOICE

1. d   2. c   3. a   4. b   5. c

SHORT ANSWER

1. raspberry, aggregate fruit; pineapple, multiple fruit; pea pod, simple fruit
2. Factors and conditions include water, oxygen, a particular range of temperatures, light, and passage through an animal's digestive tract.
3. Advantage: many new individuals can be produced in a short time, enabling clones to fill the available space. Disadvantage: since all of the offspring are genetically identical, they have the same tolerance to the environment and are attacked by the same diseases and pests.
4. The structures are runners (or stolons), rhizomes, bulbs, and tubers.
5. wind dispersal: orchid seeds, milkweed seeds; animal dispersal: fruit; water dispersal: coconuts
6. Plant embryos must grow to the soil surface before they can capture enough light to carry out photosynthesis. This growth requires energy, which is provided by the food reserves in the seed.

STRUCTURES AND FUNCTIONS

a, endosperm; b, seed coat; c, cotyledon; d, plumule; e, hypocotyl; f, radicle

Section 31-1
VOCABULARY REVIEW

1. A plant hormone is a chemical messenger that affects a plant's ability to respond to its environment.
2. Apical dominance is the inhibition of lateral buds by the presence of a shoot tip.
3. Ethephon is a synthetic chemical that breaks down to release ethylene gas.
4. Abscission is the detachment of leaves, flowers, or fruits from a plant.
5. A cytokinin is a hormone that promotes cell division.

MULTIPLE CHOICE

1. b   2. d   3. a   4. c   5. a

SHORT ANSWER

1. The seeds produce IAA, which stimulates the development of the fruit; removing the seeds removes the IAA.
2. Gibberellins make plants grow taller, increase the size of seedless fruit, promote uniform germination, and increase the alcohol content of beer.
3. Uses of ethylene or ethephon include ripening fruits, changing the color of citrus fruits, and promoting the abscission of fruits at harvest time.
4. ABA stimulates the transport of potassium ions out of guard cells, causing stomata to close. This reduces the amount of water that evaporates through the stomata.
5. Abscisic acid induces dormancy in buds, maintains dormancy in seeds, and makes leaves effectively dormant by closing their stomata.

STRUCTURES AND FUNCTIONS

The plant on the right was treated with a gibberellin. It is much taller than the one on the left. Gibberellins cause plants to grow to a taller-than-normal height.

Section 31-2
VOCABULARY REVIEW

1. Thigmotropism is a plant's growth response to touching a solid object, for example, tendrils and stems of vines coil when they touch an object.
2. A thigmonastic movement is a type of nastic movement that occurs in response to touching a plant, for example, a Venus' flytrap closes its leaves when touched.
3. A nyctinastic movement is one that occurs in response to the daily cycle of light and dark, for example, the prayer plant's leaves are vertical at night and horizontal during the day.

MULTIPLE CHOICE

1. a   2. c   3. b   4. d   5. b

SHORT ANSWER

1. Positive phototropism maximizes the amount of light that can be absorbed by a plant. Positive gravitropism causes roots to grow into the soil, where they can absorb water and nutrients.
2. auxins
3. Nastic movements are caused by the movement of water into or out of cells, which changes the pressure inside the cells.
4. Thigmonastic movements allow plants to capture prey, discourage insect feeding, and reduce water loss.
5. Insect capture requires the leaves to close rapidly. A thigmonastic movement is fast enough to accomplish this, but not thigmotropic movement.

STRUCTURES AND FUNCTIONS

1. The shoot is exhibiting positive phototropism and negative gravitropism; the root is exhibiting positive gravitropism.
2. Auxins are involved in these responses.

Section 31-3

VOCABULARY REVIEW

1. Photoperiodism is an organism's response to changes in the length of days and nights.
2. Vernalization is the stimulation of flowering by low temperatures.
3. Bolting is the rapid elongation of a flowering stem.
4. Critical night length is the requirement many plants have for a specific amount of darkness or night length.

MULTIPLE CHOICE

1. c   2. d   3. b   4. a   5. b

SHORT ANSWER

1. flowering, formation of storage organs, and bud dormancy
2. SDPs: ragweed, poinsettias, chrysanthemums, goldenrods, and soybeans; they flower in the spring or fall. LDPs: wheat, radishes, asters, irises, and beets; they flower in the summer.
3. Answers include photoperiodism, flowering, bud dormancy, and seed germination.
4. Protect them from exposure to low temperatures.
5. Spinach will flower in the northern United States during the summer, when the nights are shorter than 10 h. Flowering is undesirable in spinach, because it is grown for its leaves, not its flowers.

STRUCTURES AND FUNCTIONS

a, no; b. yes; c, yes; d, no; e, no; f, yes

Section 32-1

VOCABULARY REVIEW

1. A vertebrate is an animal with a backbone.
2. Ingestion is the process in which an animal takes in organic material, usually in the form of other living things.
3. A dorsal nerve cord is a hollow tube lying just above the notochord.
4. Cephalization is the concentration of sensory and brain structures in the anterior end.

MULTIPLE CHOICE

1. a   2. c   3. d   4. a   5. b

SHORT ANSWER

1. During differentiation, the cells of a multicellular organism become different from each other; these differences enable the cells to specialize in performing different functions.
2. They group animals based on the animal's evolutionary history, which is inferred from morphology, fossils, RNA, and other factors.
3. As a cephalized animal moves through its environment, sensory structures concentrated on the head can sense the environment.
4. A coelom provides a structure against which muscles can contract, allows the exterior of the body to move more freely with respect to the internal organs, and acts as a reservoir and medium of transport for nutrients and wastes.
5. Some similarities that indicate evolutionary relatedness may be present during development but not in adulthood. Ignoring development might then lead to errors in classification.

STRUCTURES AND FUNCTIONS

a, dorsal; b, anterior; c, posterior; d, ventral
This animal has bilateral symmetry.

Section 32-2

VOCABULARY REVIEW

1. *Segmentation* refers to a body composed of repeating similar units; in vertebrates, segmentation is evident in the vertebrae.
2. An integument is an outer covering of an animal; an exoskeleton functions as an integument for animals such as arthropods and some mollusks.

MULTIPLE CHOICE

1. c   2. d   3. c   4. a   5. b

SHORT ANSWER

1. Annelida, Arthropoda, and Chordata
2. Both must eliminate ammonia, which is very toxic. Some animals convert ammonia to less toxic substances.
3. The legs of a deer are positioned directly beneath its body, giving the deer greater mobility and speed on land; the integument of a reptile is largely watertight, minimizing loss of water to the environment.
4. It separates oxygenated and deoxygenated blood, thus improving the efficiency of the circulatory system.
5. Advantage: any two hermaphrodites can mate with each other, and some hermaphrodites can fertilize their own eggs. Disadvantage: with self-fertilization, no genetic variability is introduced by the mating because both gametes come from the same individual.

STRUCTURES AND FUNCTIONS

a, kidney; b, allows gas exchange between the blood and the environment; c, integument; d, processes sensory information, coordinates behavior, makes decisions; e, endoskeleton

Section 32-3

VOCABULARY REVIEW

1. The archenteron is a deep cavity in the gastrula and becomes the gut. The blastopore is the opening to the archenteron.
2. In a pseudocoelom, mesoderm lines the interior of the coelom but does not surround the gut. Both the interior of the coelom and the gut are lined by mesoderm.
3. In a protostome, the blastopore develops into a mouth; in a deuterostome, the blastopore develops into an anus.
4. In schizocoely, the mesoderm forms from cells that split away from the junction of the endoderm and ectoderm; in enterocoely, the mesoderm forms when cells lining the dorsal part of the coelom begin dividing rapidly.

MULTIPLE CHOICE

1. b   2. a   3. c   4. d   5. c

SHORT ANSWER

1. A blastula is a hollow ball of cells; a gastrula is a cup-shaped structure consisting of an outer layer of ectoderm surrounding an inner layer of endoderm, which in turn surrounds a deep cavity.

2. ectoderm, mesoderm, and endoderm
3. Both echinoderms and chordates are deuterostomes. Most deuterostomes undergo radial cleavage, indeterminate cleavage, and exhibit enterocoely.
4. If more than one sperm entered the egg, the egg nucleus would contain more than two sets of chromosomes. Normal mitosis could not occur, and the zygote would fail to develop normally.

STRUCTURES AND FUNCTIONS

a, protostome; b, deuterostome; c, schizocoely; d, enterocoely; e, mouth; f, anus

Section 33-1

VOCABULARY REVIEW

1. A choanocyte is a type of flagellated cell that lines the interior of a sponge and draws water into the sponge.
2. The osculum is the opening at the top of a sponge where water exits the sponge.
3. A spicule is a tiny, hard particle of calcium carbonate or silicon dioxide that makes up the skeleton of some sponges.
4. An amoebocyte is a type of cell that crawls about within the body wall of a sponge and aids in feeding and reproduction.

MULTIPLE CHOICE

1. d   2. b   3. d   4. a   5. c

SHORT ANSWER

1. Invertebrates are defined solely on the basis of what they lack—a backbone—rather than on the basis of characteristics they share.
2. A sponge's skeleton may be made of spongin or spicules (or both). Spongin is a network of protein fibers, while spicules are tiny, hard particles made of calcium carbonate or silicon dioxide.
3. Choanocytes engulf sperm and transfer them to amoebocytes, which carry the sperm to an egg.
4. Since all hermaphrodites produce eggs, the chances of successful fertilization are greater than they would be if only half the population produced eggs.
5. Larvae would be better, since their flagella enable them to swim away from the parent sponge and produce another sponge in a new location.

STRUCTURES AND FUNCTIONS

a, osculum; b, amoebocyte; c, choanocyte; d, ostium; e, spicules

Section 33-2

VOCABULARY REVIEW

1. A polyp is the vase-shaped form of a cnidarian; a medusa is the bell-shaped form of a cnidarian.
2. The epidermis is the outer cell layer of a cnidarian; the gastrodermis is the inner cell layer.
3. Mesoglea is a jellylike material between the epidermis and gastrodermis in a cnidarian; a planula is the ciliated larva of some cnidarians.
4. A cnidocyte is a specialized cnidarian cell used for defense and capturing prey; a nematocyst is an organelle inside a cnidocyte that contains a long, coiled filament.
5. A colloblast is a cell found in ctenophores that secretes a sticky substance to bind prey; an apical organ is a sensory structure at one end of a ctenophore's body.

MULTIPLE CHOICE

1. a   2. c   3. d   4. b   5. c

SHORT ANSWER

1. Some nematocysts have filaments with sharp tips and spines that can puncture prey and inject poison; others have filaments that can wrap around prey.
2. Hydras exist only as polyps, are not colonial, and live in fresh water.
3. The medusa is the dominant body form in the life cycle of a scyphozoan. The polyp is the dominant body form in the life cycle of an anthozoan.
4. The clownfish live among sea anemones. The anemones' stinging tentacles protect the clownfish from predators, and the clownfish drives away other fish that try to feed on the anemone. Algae live inside corals. The corals supply algae with nutrients, and the algae supply the corals with oxygen.
5. Each polyp cements its skeleton to the skeletons of adjoining polyps in the colony. When the polyps die, their skeletons remain, and build up into a reef.
6. No; the hydras are green because they contain algae, which require light to carry out photosynthesis.

STRUCTURES AND FUNCTIONS

a, epidermis; b, mesoglea; c, gastrovascular cavity; d, gastrodermis; e, tentacle; f, mouth; the medusa

Section 34-1

VOCABULARY REVIEW

1. A proglottid is a body section of a tapeworm and contains male and female reproductive structures; a tegument is a continuous sheet of fused cells that covers the external surface of a fluke.
2. Cerebral ganglia are clusters of nerve cells that serve as a brain; eyespots are cup-shaped structures that sense light.
3. A primary host is a host from which an adult parasite derives its nourishment and in which sexual reproduction occurs; an intermediate host is a host from which the larvae of a parasite derive their nourishment.

MULTIPLE CHOICE

1. c   2. b   3. d   4. a   5. d

SHORT ANSWER

1. Flame cells collect excess water, which is then transported through excretory tubules and excreted from numerous pores scattered over the body surface.
2. Planarians detect the intensity and direction of light with two eyespots; tapeworms cannot detect light.
3. The primary host is a human; the intermediate host is a snail. The fluke enters its primary host as a tailed larva that penetrates the host's skin.
4. the larval stage
5. The eggs sometimes block blood vessels, causing a disease that may kill the host. A parasite that kills its host may not be perfectly adapted to its environment.

STRUCTURES AND FUNCTIONS

a, scolex; b, sucker; c, neck; d, proglottid; e, ovary; f, uterus; g, testes

Section 34-2

VOCABULARY REVIEW

1. Trichinosis is a human disease caused by eating undercooked meat (pork) containing cysts of the *Trichinella* worm.
2. A filarial worm is a parasitic roundworm that causes diseases such as elephantiasis in humans and heartworm disease in dogs.
3. A mastax is a muscular organ that breaks up food in a rotifer.

MULTIPLE CHOICE

1. b   2. c   3. a   4. d   5. a

SHORT ANSWER

1. Food moves through a digestive tract in only one direction, which allows different parts of the tract to carry out different functions.
2. *Ascaris* eggs and pinworm eggs hatch in the intestine; hookworm eggs hatch in warm, damp soil.
3. the mosquito
4. The crown of cilia looks like a pair of rotating wheels. It sweeps food into the digestive tract.
5. The small intestine often contains undigested and partially digested food on which the worm can feed.

STRUCTURES AND FUNCTIONS

a, cilia; b, excretory tubule; c, stomach; d, anus; e, mastax; f, ovary; g, cloaca

Section 35-1

VOCABULARY REVIEW

1. The visceral mass of a mollusk contains the heart and organs of digestion, excretion, and reproduction. The visceral mass is covered by a layer of epidermis called the mantle.
2. Hemolymph is the fluid in an open circulatory system; a hemocoel is a set of hemolymph-filled spaces in the tissues of an animal with an open circulatory system.
3. The incurrent siphon of a bivalve takes in water that contains oxygen and nutrients. Water exiting through the excurrent siphon carries wastes from the body.

MULTIPLE CHOICE

1. d   2. c   3. b   4. a   5. b

SHORT ANSWER

1. The two main regions are the head-foot and the visceral mass. The visceral mass contains most of the internal organs. The head-foot is directly involved with locomotion.
2. The mantle secretes the protective shell.
3. Gastropods use their radula to cut through leaves, scrape up algae, drill holes through the shells of other mollusks, and harpoon prey; bivalves filter small organisms from the water that passes through their gills.
4. Marine clams shed sperm and eggs into the water, and fertilization occurs externally. In most freshwater clams, eggs are fertilized internally by sperm that enter through the incurrent siphon.
5. A typical molluskan shell is secreted by the mantle, consists of calcium carbonate, is formed by both males and females, and protects the entire animal.

STRUCTURES AND FUNCTIONS

a, shell; b, gill; c, mantle cavity; d, anus; e, heart; f, mantle; g, stomach; h, ganglia

Section 35-2

VOCABULARY REVIEW

1. A seta is an external bristle on an annelid.
2. A parapodium is a fleshy protrusion on an annelid.
3. A typhlosole is an infolding of the intestinal wall in an earthworm.
4. A nephridium is an excretory tubule in an earthworm.

MULTIPLE CHOICE

1. d   2. c   3. a   4. b   5. c

SHORT ANSWER

1. The crop is a temporary storage area for ingested soil; the gizzard grinds the soil, releasing and breaking up organic matter.
2. Earthworms help release nutrients from dead matter into the soil, allow air to penetrate into the soil to reach plant roots and soil microorganisms, and loosen the soil, which makes it easier for roots to penetrate and water to seep in.
3. They contract and force blood through the circulatory system.
4. A leech attaches its anterior sucker and then pulls the rest of its body forward.
5. The host would probably be an animal with a high body temperature, such as a mammal or a bird. Moving toward warmth would increase the leech's chances of finding a suitable host.

STRUCTURES AND FUNCTIONS

a, crop; b, gizzard; c, aortic arches; d, pharynx; e, cerebral ganglion; f, nephridia; g, longitudinal muscle; h, circular muscle

Section 36-1

VOCABULARY REVIEW

1. An arthropod is a segmented animal with jointed appendages and an exoskeleton.
2. A compound eye is an eye with many individual light detectors, each with its own lens.
3. A tagma is a body structure that is produced by the fusion of a number of smaller segments.
4. A chelicera is a pincerlike mouthpart found on some arthropods, such as spiders and scorpions.

MULTIPLE CHOICE

1. a   2. c   3. d   4. b   5. d

SHORT ANSWER

1. Wax makes the exoskeleton repel water; it is in the outer layer of the exoskeleton.
2. Calcium carbonate and chitin make the exoskeleton hard; they are in the middle layer of the exoskeleton.
3. legs, antennae, mandibles, and chelicerae
4. The anterior end of the body has food-handling appendages, antennae, compound eyes, structures that sense light intensity, and a brain.
5. Members of the subphylum Crustacea have branched antennae; members of the subphylum Chelicerata have no antennae; and members of the subphylum Myriapoda have unbranched appendages, including legs. Therefore, it would be difficult to assign *Marella* to one of these subphyla.

STRUCTURES AND FUNCTIONS

from left to right: a, sea spider; b, horseshoe crab; c, scorpion; d, mite; e, spider; f, shrimp; g, centipede; h, millipede; i, insect

Section 36-2
VOCABULARY REVIEW

1. A cirrus is one of 12 modified legs on a barnacle and is used for filter feeding; a cheliped is one of two modified legs on a crayfish and is used for defense and capturing food.
2. The cephalothorax is the body section consisting of two fused tagmata, the head and thorax; the thorax consists of eight segments and lies behind the head.
3. Crustaceans have two types of feelers. Antennae are longer feelers that respond to touch and taste; antennules are shorter feelers that are sensitive to touch, taste, and balance.
4. Swimmerets are appendages attached to the anterior abdominal segments of a crayfish and function in reproduction; the telson is part of the paddlelike tail on the posterior end of a crayfish.

MULTIPLE CHOICE

1. b   2. c   3. d   4. a   5. b

SHORT ANSWER

1. A nauplius has three pairs of appendages and a single eye in the middle of its head.
2. A barnacle extends its cirri through openings in its shell, sweeping small organisms and food particles from the water into its mouth.
3. The mandibles chew food; the maxillae manipulate food and draw water currents over the gills; and the maxillipeds touch, taste, and manipulate food.
4. Hemolymph flows from the heart through several large vessels to different regions of the body, where it leaves the vessels and enters spaces within the body. The hemolymph then passes through the gills and returns to the heart.
5. By lying on its side near the surface, the crayfish exposes the gills on that side to the oxygenated water at the surface. By moving the walking legs on that side, the crayfish circulates this water over its gills.

STRUCTURES AND FUNCTIONS

a, green gland; b, brain; c, stomach; d, heart; e, ovary; f, digestive gland; g, intestine

Section 36-3
VOCABULARY REVIEW

1. An arachnid is a member of the class Arachnida, which includes spiders, scorpions, mites, and ticks.
2. A pedipalp is an appendage on the cephalothorax of an arachnid; it is used to hold food and chew.
3. A spiracle is an opening in the exoskeleton of a terrestrial arthropod through which the tracheae open to the environment.
4. A Malpighian tubule is the main excretory organ of a terrestrial arthropod.
5. In spiders, a spinneret is an organ that connects to silk glands in the abdomen and is used to secrete silk for spinning webs, building nests, and protecting eggs.

6. Book lungs are paired sacs in the abdomen with many parallel folds that resemble the pages of a book and function in gas exchange.

MULTIPLE CHOICE

1. c   2. a   3. b   4. d   5. a

SHORT ANSWER

1. to snare prey, to wrap prey, to build nests, to protect eggs, and to pull themselves through the air
2. Book lungs are paired sacs with many parallel folds that resemble the pages of a book; their function is to exchange gases with the environment.
3. The black widow has a bright red or orange hourglass-shaped mark on the ventral surface of its abdomen. The brown recluse has a violin-shaped mark on the dorsal surface of its cephalothorax.
4. Centipedes have long legs, which enable them to move quickly, and poison claws, which enable them to kill prey.
5. Mites and ticks support this idea. They are the smallest and most abundant arachnids. Mites can live in fresh water, in the sea, and on land; some are free living, while others are parasites of plants or animals.

STRUCTURES AND FUNCTIONS

a, stomach; b, poison gland; c, chelicera (fang); d, pedipalp; e, Malpighian tubule; f, silk gland; g, gut; h, book lung

Section 37-1
VOCABULARY REVIEW

1. Both are insect mouthparts; the labrum functions like an upper lip, and the labium functions like a lower lip.
2. The tympanum is a large oval membrane for sensing sound; the ovipositor is the last segment on a female's abdomen and is used to lay eggs.
3. In incomplete metamorphosis, a nymph hatches from an egg and undergoes a gradual change in body form to become an adult; in complete metamorphosis, an insect undergoes two major stages of development between egg and adult.
4. A nymph is an immature form of an insect that looks somewhat like the adult, but it is smaller, and its wings and reproductive organs are undeveloped; a pupa is a stage of development in which an insect changes from a larva to an adult.

MULTIPLE CHOICE

1. d   2. b   3. a   4. c   5. b

SHORT ANSWER

1. Shared characteristics include mandibles, one pair of antennae, and unbranched appendages. Differences (in most insects) include the presence of wings; only three pairs of legs; a body divided into head, thorax, and abdomen; and a life cycle that includes metamorphosis.
2. Termites feed on decaying wood, thereby recycling nutrients needed to maintain a healthy forest.
3. The salivary glands secrete saliva, which moistens food. The gastric ceca secrete enzymes into the midgut, where food is digested.
4. A chrysalis encloses a butterfly pupa; a cocoon encloses a moth pupa.

5. To produce eggs, female mosquitoes must have a source of protein, which is present in large amounts in blood but not in sap or nectar. Male mosquitoes do not have this requirement.

STRUCTURES AND FUNCTIONS

a, simple eye; b, compound eye; c, thorax; d, tympanum; e, spiracles; f, ovipositor; g, abdomen

Section 37-2
VOCABULARY REVIEW

1. A pheromone is a chemical that is released by an animal and that affects the behavior or development of other members of the same species.
2. Innate behavior is behavior that is genetically determined.
3. Royal jelly is a high-protein substance that worker honeybees secrete and feed to the queen and the youngest larvae.
4. The queen factor is a pheromone secreted by a queen honeybee that prevents other female larvae from developing into queens.
5. Kin selection is a mechanism of increasing the propagation of one's own genes by helping a closely related individual reproduce.

MULTIPLE CHOICE

1. b   **2.** d   **3.** c   **4.** a   **5.** d

SHORT ANSWER

1. Male mosquitoes and moths use their antennae to find distant females. Mosquitoes detect buzzing sounds; male moths detect pheromones.
2. Male crickets produce several calls that differ from those of other cricket species.
3. Workers and the queen are female; the workers are sterile.
4. when the honey supply begins to run low
5. Close relatives share many genes with the individual who performs the altruistic behavior, including the genes that code for that behavior. Those genes will remain in the population if the relatives reproduce successfully.

STRUCTURES AND FUNCTIONS

a, round dance, which indicates that a food source is near the hive; b, waggle dance, which indicates the direction and distance to a food source

Section 38-1
VOCABULARY REVIEW

1. An ossicle is a calcium carbonate plate that makes up the endoskeleton of an echinoderm; a test is the compact, rigid endoskeleton of a sea urchin or sand dollar.
2. A tube foot is a small, movable extension of an echinoderm's water-vascular system that aids in movement; an ampulla is a bulblike sac at the upper end of each tube foot.
3. Both are parts of a sea star's digestive tract; the cardiac stomach can be turned inside out to partially digest food outside the sea star, and the pyloric stomach completes food digestion inside the sea star.
4. The water-vascular system is a network of water-filled canals that aid movement. The radial canal is part of the water-vascular system and carries water to the tube feet in the arms.

MULTIPLE CHOICE

1. d   **2.** c   **3.** a   **4.** b   **5.** b

SHORT ANSWER

1. Echinoderm larvae are bilaterally symmetrical, which indicates that echinoderms probably evolved from bilaterally symmetrical ancestors.
2. basket star, Ophiuroidea; sea star, Asteroidea; feather star, Crinoidea; brittle star, Ophiuroidea
3. A nerve ring circles the mouth, a radial nerve runs from the nerve ring along the length of each arm, and a nerve net extends near the body surface. The sea star also has an eyespot near the end of each arm and several tentacles that respond to touch.
4. Eggs are fertilized externally and develop into free-swimming larvae. The larvae settle down and develop into adults.
5. A sea star may shed an arm at its base if the arm is captured by a predator.
6. Since sea stars are radially symmetrical, no particular part of a sea star always leads when the animal moves through its environment. Therefore, there is no advantage to having sensory structures and a neural center concentrated at one end.

STRUCTURES AND FUNCTIONS

a, skin gill; b, spine; c, pedicellaria; d, tube feet; e, sensory tentacles; f, eyespot

Section 38-2
VOCABULARY REVIEW

1. A notochord is a stiff, flexible rod of cells that runs the length of the body near the dorsal surface of a chordate.
2. A lancelet is a blade-shaped chordate belonging to the subphylum Cephalochordata.
3. A tunicate is a sessile, barrel-shaped chordate belonging to the subphylum Urochordata.
4. An atriopore is an opening through which water leaves the body of a lancelet.

MULTIPLE CHOICE

1. a   **2.** c   **3.** b   **4.** d   **5.** c

SHORT ANSWER

1. a notochord, a dorsal nerve cord, pharyngeal pouches, and a postanal tail
2. Lancelets use their tail to swim weakly and to wriggle backward into the sand.
3. Tunicates are protected by a tough covering called a tunic.
4. They squirt out a stream of water when touched.
5. A larval tunicate has all four chordate characteristics, but an adult tunicate has only one: a pouch-like pharynx with slits.
6. Like sponges, most adult tunicates are sessile animals that feed by filtering food from the water; they are also hermaphrodites, as are most sponges. Unlike sponges, tunicates have true tissues and organs; water enters an adult tunicate through a single opening, while it enters a sponge through numerous pores.

STRUCTURES AND FUNCTIONS

a, notochord; b, dorsal nerve cord; c, pharynx; d, atriopore; e, segmented muscles; f, postanal tail

Section 39-1

VOCABULARY REVIEW

1. A vertebra is bone or cartilage that surrounds and forms the dorsal nerve cord in the spine.
2. A cranium is a skull, which protects the brain.
3. A gill arch is a skeletal element that supports the pharynx.

MULTIPLE CHOICE

1. c   2. b   3. a   4. d   5. c   6. b

SHORT ANSWER

1. Both groups lack or lacked jaws and paired fins, and both have or had cartilaginous skeletons.
2. The skin of amphibians is thin and permeable to gases and water; the skin of reptiles is dry and scaly.
3. Horses belong to the class Mammalia; animals in that class have hair and nurse their young.
4. Jaws and paired fins appeared.
5. Fishes in the class Chondrichthyes have jaws and paired fins. Paired fins increase stability and maneuverability, and jaws make it possible to seize and manipulate prey. These adaptive advantages allowed fishes in the class Chondrichthyes to diversify into numerous species and to be more successful predators than those in the class Cephalaspidomorphi.

STRUCTURES AND FUNCTIONS

a, Myxini; b, Cephalaspidomorphi; c, Chondrichthyes; d, Actinopterygii; e, Sarcopterygii; f, Amphibia; g, Reptilia; h, Aves; i, Mammalia

Section 39-2

VOCABULARY REVIEW

1. The lateral line is a system of canals in the skin that are lined with sensory structures that detect vibrations in the water.
2. Cartilage is a flexible, lightweight material made of cells surrounded by tough fibers of protein.
3. A placoid scale is one of many small, toothlike spines that cover the skin of a cartilaginous fish.
4. Chemoreception is the ability to detect chemicals in the environment.

MULTIPLE CHOICE

1. b   2. d   3. a   4. c   5. a

SHORT ANSWER

1. A hagfish burrows into the body of a dead or dying fish or invertebrate and pinches off chunks of tissue with two movable plates and a rough tonguelike structure in its mouth.
2. Sharks that feed on large fish or mammals have large triangular teeth with sawlike edges that hook and tear flesh.
3. Cartilaginous fishes can move water over their gills by swimming with their mouth open and by expanding and contracting their mouth cavity and pharynx.
4. Fertilization in lampreys occurs outside the body of either parent, but fertilization in cartilaginous fishes occurs inside the body of the female.
5. Jawless fishes should produce more gametes since fertilization occurs externally. With external fertilization, there is a lower chance that sperm and eggs will meet. Producing more gametes increases the chances of fertilization.

STRUCTURES AND FUNCTIONS

a, caudal fin; b, dorsal fin; c, spiracle; d, nostril; e, pelvic fin; f, clasper; g, anal fin; h, gill slit; i, pectoral fin

Section 39-3

VOCABULARY REVIEW

1. A swim bladder is a gas-filled sac that many bony fishes use to control buoyancy.
2. A lobe-finned fish has fleshy fins that are supported by a series of bones with a central bony axis.
3. A ray-finned fish has fins that are supported by long, segmented, flexible, bony elements.
4. In countercurrent flow, water flows across the gill filaments in a direction opposite to blood flow.

MULTIPLE CHOICE

1. a   2. c   3. b   4. d   5. d

SHORT ANSWER

1. The scales grow quickly when food is abundant and grow slowly when food is scarce.
2. The kidneys and the gills are involved in maintaining water-and-ion balance.
3. A bony fish adjusts its buoyancy by varying the amount of gas in its swim bladder.
4. Fertilization occurs externally in most species.
5. Faulty valves would allow blood to flow back into the ventricle, making delivery of blood to the gills less efficient. Body cells would therefore receive less oxygen and make less ATP.

STRUCTURES AND FUNCTIONS

a, conus arteriosus; b, atrium; c, sinus venosus; d, ventricle

Two arrows should be drawn pointing to the two branches of chamber c, and one arrow should be drawn pointing away from chamber a.

Section 40-1

VOCABULARY REVIEW

1. A preadaptation is an adaptation in an ancestral group that allows a shift to new functions, which are later favored by natural selection.
2. A tadpole is a swimming, tailed larva of an anuran.

MULTIPLE CHOICE

1. c   2. a   3. d   4. a   5. d

SHORT ANSWER

1. The two groups of animals have similar skulls and vertebral columns, and the bones in the fin of a lobe-finned fish are similar to the bones in the limb of an amphibian.
2. *Ichthyostega* had a large tail fin, lateral-line canals on its head, and large, sharp teeth adapted to preying on fish.
3. Amphibians can use gills, lungs, and skin for gas exchange.
4. A frog usually has smooth, moist skin and a compact body with a short, rigid spine; a salamander also has moist skin but has an elongated body.
5. It is likely to make them clearly visible and recognizable to predators, reducing the chance that a predator will mistake them for a nonpoisonous species and attack them.

a, Anura; b, Caudata; c, Gymnophiona; d and e, frogs and toads; f, salamanders; g, caecilians

Section 40-2

VOCABULARY REVIEW

1. Pulmonary circulation carries deoxygenated blood from the heart to the lungs and back to the heart; systemic circulation carries oxygenated blood from the heart to the rest of the body and back to the heart.
2. Pulmonary respiration occurs through the lungs; cutaneous respiration occurs through the skin.
3. The duodenum is the upper portion of the small intestine; the ileum is the coiled middle portion of the small intestine.
4. Mesentery is a membrane that holds the small intestine in place; the columella is a small bone that extends between the tympanic membrane and the inner ear.
5. The nictitating membrane is a transparent, movable membrane that covers each eye; the tympanic membrane is the eardrum.

MULTIPLE CHOICE

1. d   2. b   3. a   4. c   5. b

SHORT ANSWER

1. The vertebrae interlock and form a rigid structure that can support the weight of the body.
2. In a fish, blood slows as it is pumped through the gills and then through the rest of the body. In an amphibian, blood that passes through the lungs is pumped a second time by the heart before circulating through the body.
3. The cerebrum integrates behavior and is responsible for learning; the optic lobes process information from the eyes; the cerebellum is involved in muscular coordination; the medulla oblongata controls some organ functions, such as heart rate and respiration rate.
4. The muscles of an amphibian's belly support the weight of the internal organs on land; in a fish, the weight of the organs is supported by water.

STRUCTURES AND FUNCTIONS

a, pectoral; b, urostyle; c, pelvic; d, skull;
e, spine; f, femur

Section 40-3

VOCABULARY REVIEW

1. Amplexus is a mating behavior in which a male frog climbs onto the back of a female and grasps her firmly in an embrace.
2. Thyroxine is a hormone produced by the thyroid gland and that stimulates metamorphosis in amphibians.

MULTIPLE CHOICE

1. a   2. c   3. d   4. b   5. c

SHORT ANSWER

1. Male frogs call to attract females of their own species and to warn off other males.
2. The legs grow; the tail disappears; the gills disappear; the mouth broadens; the teeth develop; the jaws develop; the lungs become functional.

3. Some salamanders remain in the larval stage for their entire life; some amphibians hatch from the egg as a small version of the adult without going through a larval stage.
4. to prevent the eggs from desiccating
5. It helps the eggs remain attached to objects in the water, which may prevent them from being carried away by currents or sinking to the bottom.

STRUCTURES AND FUNCTIONS

a, 5; b, 3; c, 6; d, 1; e, 4; f, 2

Section 41-1

VOCABULARY REVIEW

1. The amnion is a thin membrane that encloses the fluid surrounding the embryo of a reptile, mammal, or bird.
2. The allantois is a membrane in the amniotic egg that stores nitrogenous wastes produced by the embryo.
3. The chorion is a membrane that surrounds all of the other membranes in an amniotic egg and helps protect the embryo.
4. Albumen is a mixture of protein and water contained in an amniotic egg.
5. Keratin is protein in fingernails, hair, and skin.

MULTIPLE CHOICE

1. b   2. d   3. a   4. c   5. b

SHORT ANSWER

1. Sediments from the end of the Cretaceous period contain high concentrations of iridium, which is relatively abundant in asteroids. Sediments from this time also contain quartz crystals that were deformed by a powerful force. A large impact crater dating from this time exists on the Yucatán Peninsula.
2. The shell provides protection from physical damage, limits evaporation of water from the egg, and allows exchange of oxygen and carbon dioxide.
3. Whereas an amphibian's skin is thin and moist, a reptile's skin is thick and dry; this prevents water loss and protects against the wear and tear of terrestrial environments.
4. As the continents drifted to new locations on Earth's surface, their climates and vegetation changed, causing species to evolve in different directions on different continents.

STRUCTURES AND FUNCTIONS

The order from left to right is turtles, tuataras, lizards, snakes, crocodiles, dinosaurs, and birds.

Section 41-2

VOCABULARY REVIEW

1. Alveoli are numerous small sacs in the lungs.
2. Jacobson's organ is located in the roof of the mouth of reptiles and is sensitive to odors.
3. An ectotherm is an animal that warms its body by absorbing heat from its surroundings.
4. Viviparity is a reproductive pattern in which a shell does not form around the egg and the young are retained within the female's body until they are mature enough to be born.
5. A placenta is a structure through which nutrients and oxygen are transferred from the mother to the embryo.

MULTIPLE CHOICE

1. d   **2.** c   **3.** b   **4.** a   **5.** b

SHORT ANSWER

1. when it is inactive, when it is underwater, or when it needs to raise its body temperature quickly
2. A snake detects ground vibrations by transmitting the vibrations through the bones of its jaw and its columella to its inner ear.
3. A pit viper detects warm objects with the heat-sensitive pits below its eyes.
4. basking in the sun, staying in the shade, using different body positions, and panting
5. A female crocodile builds a nest, guards against predators while the eggs incubate, opens the nest when the eggs hatch, carries the hatchlings to the water in her mouth, and may protect the young for a year or more.
6. In most reptiles, the egg is enclosed in a shell inside the mother, so it must be fertilized internally before the shell is formed. In viviparous reptiles, the embryo is without a shell but develops inside the mother, so fertilization must also be internal in these reptiles.

STRUCTURES AND FUNCTIONS

a, right atrium; b, septum; c, left atrium; d, ventricle. In e, the arrow should point toward the end of the left pulmonary artery; in f, the arrow should point toward the right half of the ventricle; in g, the arrow should point toward the left half of the ventricle.

Section 41-3

VOCABULARY REVIEW

1. A carapace is the dorsal part of the shell of a turtle or tortoise.
2. Autotomy is the ability of an animal to detach its tail or other body part.
3. A constrictor is a snake that suffocates its prey by wrapping its body around the prey and squeezing each time the prey exhales.
4. An elapid is a snake that injects poison through two small, fixed fangs in the front of its mouth.

MULTIPLE CHOICE

1. a   **2.** c   **3.** c   **4.** d   **5.** b

SHORT ANSWER

1. The shell is streamlined and disk-shaped, permitting rapid turning in water; the limbs have webbed feet or have evolved into flippers for swimming and maneuvering.
2. A snake has jaws that are loosely hinged, can move independently, and can open to an angle of 130 degrees; the jaw, palate, and parts of the skull are joined by a flexible, elastic ligament.
3. A viper injects venom through large, mobile fangs in the front of its mouth that swing forward when the viper strikes.
4. *Tuatara* means "spiny crest"; tuataras, which are the only members of the order Rhynchocephalia, have a spiny crest that runs down their back.
5. Snakes move by extending and contracting the overlapping scales on their body. If a surface is very smooth, it will have no projections for the scales to push against, making it difficult for snakes to move forward.

STRUCTURES AND FUNCTIONS

a, Squamata; b, inject venom; c, Crocodilia; d, prevents water from entering the air passage; e, Squamata; f, picks up airborne particles; g, Chelonia; h, allows the head, legs, and tail to be retracted into the shell for protection; i, Squamata; j, allow the animal to cling to almost any surface; k, Squamata; l, allow the animal to swallow objects larger than its head

Section 42-1

VOCABULARY REVIEW

1. A furcula is a bone formed from the fused collarbones in a bird and is commonly called the wishbone.
2. A beak is a tough, horny sheath that covers a bird's jaws.

MULTIPLE CHOICE

1. c   **2.** a   **3.** b   **4.** b   **5.** d   **6.** a

SHORT ANSWER

1. Feathers are important for flight and for insulating a bird's body against heat loss.
2. The lungs are connected to several sets of air sacs; this arrangement ensures that oxygen-rich air is always in the lungs.
3. Similarities include a flexible, S-shaped neck, a unique ankle joint, and hollow bones.
4. One hypothesis states that the ancestors of birds were tree dwellers that evolved wings that enabled them to glide from tree to tree. Another hypothesis states that the ancestors of birds were ground dwellers; initially, their wings might have stabilized them as they leapt after prey, or they might have been used to trap or knock down prey.
5. Birds' thin-walled, hollow bones break down easily, so they are not often preserved as fossils. Also, feathers rarely leave fossil imprints.

STRUCTURES AND FUNCTIONS

The order of animals from left to right is mammals, reptiles, dinosaurs, birds.

Section 42-2

VOCABULARY REVIEW

1. The shaft of a feather emerges from the follicle and supports the structures of the feather; the vanes develop on opposite sides of the shaft and contain the branches of the feather.
2. A barb is one of many branches that arise from the shaft of a feather; a barbule is one of many projections with microscopic hooks that arise from each barb.
3. The sternum, or breastbone, is an attachment point for flight muscles; the pygostyle is the terminal fused vertebrae of the spine in a bird, and it supports the tail feathers.
4. The proventriculus is the first chamber of a bird's stomach; the gizzard is the second, muscular portion of a bird's stomach.
5. Precocial young can move about and feed themselves as soon as they hatch; altricial young hatch blind, naked, and helpless.

MULTIPLE CHOICE

1. b   **2.** c   **3.** a   **4.** b   **5.** d   **6.** d

SHORT ANSWER

1. It provides lift and aids in steering and braking.
2. A bird filters uric acid from its blood in the kidneys and transports the uric acid in ureters to the cloaca, where the acid mixes with undigested matter from the intestines before it is eliminated.
3. It permits better binocular vision, meaning that depth can be perceived in the area where the visual fields of the two eyes overlap.
4. position of the stars or the sun, topographical landmarks, Earth's magnetic field, changes in air pressure due to altitude, and low-frequency sounds
5. Because the preen gland contains oil that is needed to keep the feathers smooth and water-resistant, the feathers would dry out and lose their smooth contour. This, in turn, would affect the bird's ability to fly and reduce its protection against wet or damp conditions.

STRUCTURES AND FUNCTIONS

a, proventriculus; b, gizzard; c, kidney; d, large intestine; e, cloaca; f, crop; g, heart

Section 42-3

VOCABULARY REVIEW

1. A syrinx is a structure located at the base of a bird's trachea that produces songs.
2. Crop milk is a nutritious milklike fluid secreted by the crop of birds in the order Columbiformes.

MULTIPLE CHOICE

1. d **2.** a **3.** c **4.** b **5.** d **6.** b

SHORT ANSWER

1. A kestrel has talons that enable it to grip and kill prey; a goose has webbed feet that it uses for paddling and swimming.
2. Raptors are members of the order Ciconiiformes and include ospreys, hawks, falcons, vultures, and eagles; raptors are found throughout the world.
3. Passerines have a rear toe that is enlarged and particularly flexible; this allows the feet to provide a better grip on branches.
4. They suggest that homing pigeons rely on the position of the sun and Earth's magnetic field to navigate. When the sun is visible, the birds can navigate. When the sun is not visible, presence of the magnet interferes with their ability to use Earth's magnetic field.

STRUCTURES AND FUNCTIONS

hawk, Ciconiiformes; blue jay, Passeriformes; great blue heron, Ciconiiformes; owl, Strigiformes; mallard, Anseriformes

Section 43-1

VOCABULARY REVIEW

1. A mammary gland is a milk-producing, modified sweat gland located on the thorax or abdomen of a mammal.
2. A monotreme is a member of the group of oviparous mammals.
3. A marsupial is a viviparous mammal in which the young develop within a pouch on the mother's body for some time after birth.

MULTIPLE CHOICE

1. c **2.** a **3.** b **4.** d **5.** a

SHORT ANSWER

1. Hair insulates the body against heat loss.
2. a single opening in the outer layer of its skull behind the eye socket, a saillike structure on its back, and a mouth with long bladelike teeth in the front and smaller teeth toward the back
3. Like modern terrestrial mammals but unlike *Dimetrodon*, *Lycaenops* had limbs positioned directly beneath its body. *Lycaenops* also had endothermic metabolism and hair.
4. Cretaceous period: dinosaurs; today: mammals; The extinction of the dinosaurs is responsible for this change.
5. Fossil evidence shows that early mammals were small; they had large eye sockets, suggesting that they were active at night. Small animals tend to lose body heat quickly because of their large surface-area-to-volume ratio. Body hair would have helped early mammals retain body heat.

STRUCTURES AND FUNCTIONS

The skull on the left is from the group that gave rise to mammals; it has a single opening in the skull just behind the eye socket and teeth in different parts of the jaw that are modified for different functions. The skull on the right is from the group that gave rise to modern reptiles; its teeth are uniform in size and shape.

Section 43-2

VOCABULARY REVIEW

1. The diaphragm is a sheet of muscle below the rib cage of a mammal. It functions to draw air into the lungs.
2. Baleen is a set of thin plates of keratin material that hang from the upper jaw of some whales.
3. Echolocation is a process by which some mammals locate objects by emitting high-frequency sound waves and analyzing the returning echoes.
4. A rumen is a chamber in the stomach of some herbivorous mammals; it contains microorganisms that digest cellulose.

MULTIPLE CHOICE

1. b **2.** a **3.** c **4.** d **5.** a

SHORT ANSWER

1. Mammalian lungs have a large internal surface area for gas exchange; this enables the lungs to supply oxygen rapidly to sustain a rapid metabolism.
2. Microorganisms that live in the rumen or cecum break down the cellulose contained in plants, producing small molecules that can be absorbed into the mammal's bloodstream.
3. the cerebrum; it evaluates input from the sense organs, controls movement, initiates and regulates behavior, and is involved in memory and learning
4. When a fertilized egg attaches to the lining of the uterus, extensions from the chorion grow into the lining and are surrounded by blood vessels from the uterus.

5. Animals in the north generally encounter colder weather; their small extremities have small surface-area-to-volume ratios and thus are adapted to conserving body heat. Animals in the south generally encounter hotter weather; their large extremities have large surface-area-to-volume ratios and thus are adapted to dissipating body heat.

STRUCTURES AND FUNCTIONS

a, right atrium; b, right ventricle; c, left atrium; d, left ventricle; e, septum; f, away from heart; g, toward heart; h, away from heart; i, away from heart; j, toward heart; k, away from heart; l, toward heart

Section 43-3

VOCABULARY REVIEW

1. A pinniped is an aquatic carnivore, such as a seal.
2. An ungulate is a mammal with hooves.

MULTIPLE CHOICE

1. a　**2.** b　**3.** d　**4.** c　**5.** b　**6.** a

SHORT ANSWER

1. The order is Artiodactyla. The animal is more likely to have four toes than three.
2. order Primates; most primates are omnivores, have teeth suited for a varied diet, have large brains, have forward-facing eyes, and have grasping hands and feet.
3. The small size of shrews causes them to lose body heat quickly. To maintain a constant, high body temperature, they must have a high metabolic rate. Therefore, they must eat frequently.

STRUCTURES AND FUNCTIONS

dolphin, Cetacea; bat, Chiroptera; opossum, Marsupialia; platypus, Monotremata; bear, Carnivora; elephant, Proboscidea

Section 43-4

VOCABULARY REVIEW

1. A prehensile appendage is an appendage, such as hands, feet, or tails, that can grasp.
2. An opposable thumb can touch the other fingers.
3. Bipedalism is the tendency to walk upright on two legs.
4. A hominid is a human or extinct humanlike anthropoid species.

MULTIPLE CHOICE

1. c　**2.** a　**3.** b　**4.** d　**5.** a

SHORT ANSWER

1. large, complex brain relative to size; acute color vision, binocular vision; generalist teeth allowing varied diet; broad range of visual and vocal communication; infant care; manual dexterity, with opposable thumb; complex social organization; ability to sit upright, cling to trees, hang from branches
2. Rotating shoulder and elbow joints allow a wide range of motion, including swinging from trees. An opposable thumb allows precise manipulation of objects. An opposable big toe in nonhuman anthropoids allows for grasping with the feet. The dental formula allows for a varied diet.

3. The human skeleton has an S-shaped spine for upright posture, bowl-shaped pelvis that supports the internal organs during walking, and aligned toes.
4. According to the multiregional hypothesis, local populations of *H. erectus* gave rise to local populations of *H. sapiens* all over the world, and interbreeding among populations was sufficient to maintain a single human species. According to the recent-African-origin hypothesis, *H. sapiens* evolved from *H. erectus* uniquely in Africa, then migrated out of Africa and populated the globe.
5. Because human evolution did not proceed as a single lineage of increasingly humanlike forms, finding a single form that links present-day humans with a hominid ancestor (a missing link) is not possible.

STRUCTURES AND FUNCTIONS

a. 1,400 cm^3; b. C-shaped; c. bowl-shaped; d. opposable big toe; e. smaller

Section 44-1

VOCABULARY REVIEW

1. An innate behavior is an inherited action that is performed effectively the first time without being taught; instinctive behavior.
2. A fixed action pattern is a rigid innate behavior that all members of a species perform the same way each time they perform it.
3. Habituation is a simple type of learning in which an animal learns to ignore a harmless stimulus.
4. Operant conditioning is learning by trial and error and involves associating an action with a punishment or reward.
5. Imprinting is a form of learning in which a young animal forms permanent associations with its environment during a sensitive period.

MULTIPLE CHOICE

1. c　**2.** d　**3.** d　**4.** a　**5.** a

SHORT ANSWER

1. What causes the behavior? What is the role of genes in the behavior? What is the behavior's evolutionary history? How does the behavior affect survival and reproduction?
2. Adult male lions will kill cubs that are not their own in order to mate with females of the pride and produce more offspring males who do not kill cubs. Thus, natural selection favors the alleles that cause male lions to kill cubs.
3. web-building in orb spiders, response of a hognose snake to a predator, egg retrieval in Greylag geese
4. Habituation saves energy and preserves defenses in the event of a genuine emergency.
5. Using a computer is a learned behavior that frequently involves operant conditioning, or trial-and-error learning. It may involve habituation to certain sounds the computer makes. It may involve problem-solving learned by watching others use the computer.

STRUCTURES AND FUNCTIONS

a. innate; b. egg retrieval in Greylag geese; c. habituation; d. learned; e. learned; f. pressing a lever to get food; g. learned; h. salivating in response to a bell tone; i. reasoning; j. learned; k. imprinting; l. learned

Section 44-2

VOCABULARY REVIEW

1. A dominance hierarchy is the ranking of individuals in a group to minimize conflict.
2. Aposematic coloration is having bright colors that often serve as a warning that the animal is poisonous.
3. A pheromone is a chemical released by an animal that causes individuals of the same species to react in a predictable way.
4. A circadian rhythm is a daily biological cycle.

MULTIPLE CHOICE

1. d　　**2.** d　　**3.** a　　**4.** c　　**5.** b

SHORT ANSWER

1. Aggressive behavior usually results in one animal surrendering to the other and both leaving the conflict unhurt.
2. Monogamy would be favored when it is advantageous for both parents to participate in raising the young.
3. The cost of parental care is the large energy investment by the parent, which results in fewer young being provided with care. The benefit is that it increases the likelihood that young will survive to adulthood.
4. phonemes (sounds that can be combined to form words); productivity (combinations of phonemes that produce different meanings); grammar (rules for combining words that affect meaning)
5. The behaviors can be explained by the optimality hypothesis. The availability of pine seeds affected the food-gathering behavior of the crossbills: when pine seeds were abundant, the birds remained in one tree; when pine seeds were scarce, the birds moved from tree to tree.

STRUCTURES AND FUNCTIONS

a. altruism; b. circadian rhythm; c. migration; d. courtship behavior; e. aggressive behavior; f. territorial behavior; g. dominance hierarchy

Section 45-1

VOCABULARY REVIEW

1. It senses changes in the internal and external environment, interprets sensory information, causes the body to move in response to sensory information, and coordinates voluntary and involuntary activities and regulation of some body processes.
2. It provides structure and support, moves trunks and limbs, and moves substances through the body.
3. It moves the bones in the trunk, limbs, and face.
4. It lines or covers all internal and external body surfaces, providing a protective barrier.
5. It binds, supports, and protects structures in the body.

MULTIPLE CHOICE

1. c　　**2.** a　　**3.** d　　**4.** d　　**5.** c

SHORT ANSWER

1. skeletal, smooth, and cardiac
2. Tissues compose organs, and organs compose organ systems.
3. Connective tissue is characterized by cells that are embedded in matrix.

4. Nervous tissue receives and transmits messages in the form of electrical impulses.
5. Yes; for example, the skin has several functions. As part of the integumentary system, it protects against pathogens and helps regulate body temperature. As part of the excretory system, it excretes waste products.

STRUCTURES AND FUNCTIONS

1. a, cranial cavity; b, spinal cavity; c, thoracic cavity; d, abdominal cavity; e, pelvic cavity
2. the spinal cavity and cranial cavity
3. They protect delicate internal organs and permit some organs, such as the lungs, to expand and contract while remaining securely supported.

Section 45-2

VOCABULARY REVIEW

1. The axial skeleton consists of the skull, ribs, spine, and sternum. The appendicular skeleton consists of bones of the arms, legs, scapula, clavicle, and pelvis.
2. Periosteum covers the bone's surface. Compact bone is the hard material under the periosteum. Both tissues enable bones to withstand stress.
3. Both are contained within the core of a bone.
4. Bones elongate as ossification of cartilage cells occurs at the epiphyseal plates.
5. Ligaments hold the bones of a joint in place.

MULTIPLE CHOICE

1. a　　**2.** c　　**3.** b　　**4.** a　　**5.** d

SHORT ANSWER

1. Bones provide structure and support, give shape and structure to the body, protect internal organs, and provide a framework for muscles.
2. ball and socket, shoulder; hinge joint, elbow; saddle joint, thumbs; pivot joint, top two vertebrae of the human spine; gliding joint, small bones of foot
3. Red bone marrow produces red and white blood cells, and yellow bone marrow serves as an energy reserve.
4. Bone growth is dependent on the availability of calcium. The bones store calcium. If calcium is needed elsewhere in the body, it is taken from the bones. Therefore, calcium intake is necessary to maintain bone health.

STRUCTURES AND FUNCTIONS

1. a, skull; b, clavicle; c, scapula; d, sternum; e, ribs; f, humerus; g, pelvis; h, radius; i, ulna; j, carpals; k, metacarpals; l, phalanges; m, femur; n, patella; o, tibia; p, fibula; q, tarsals; r, metatarsals; s, phalanges
2. The skeleton provides structure and support, gives shape and structure to the body, protects internal organs, and provides a framework for muscles.
3. Bone cells gradually replace the cartilage at the epiphyseal plates, which are located at the end of long bones and which consist of cartilage cells that divide and form columns, pushing older cells toward the middle of the bone.

Section 45-3

VOCABULARY REVIEW

1. Voluntary muscles can usually be controlled consciously, but involuntary muscles cannot be controlled consciously.

2. The origin is where the muscle attaches to the stationary bone. The insertion is where the muscle attaches to the moving bone.
3. A flexor is a muscle that bends a joint. An extensor is a muscle that straightens a joint.
4. Myosin is a protein that makes up the thick filaments in myofibrils, whereas actin is a protein that makes up the thin filaments of myofibrils.
5. Muscle fatigue is the physiological inability of a muscle to contract. Oxygen debt is a temporary lack of oxygen availability due to sustained strenuous exercise.

MULTIPLE CHOICE

1. b   **2.** c   **3.** d   **4.** a   **5.** a

SHORT ANSWER

1. through sustained exertion; this occurs if the respiratory and circulatory systems are not able to supply the body with sufficient oxygen to maintain ATP synthesis
2. Myosin and actin filaments interact to shorten the length of a sarcomere. A nerve impulse causes the heads of the myosin filaments to attach to points between the beads of the actin filaments, bending the heads inward and pulling the actin filaments with them. Synchronized shortening of sarcomeres in a muscle causes the muscle to contract.
3. Skeletal muscle tissue is made of elongated cells called muscle fibers. Each fiber has many nuclei. The fibers are crossed by light and dark stripes, which give the tissue its striped appearance. Smooth muscle tissue is made of spindle-shaped cells with a single nucleus that form sheets of muscle tissue. Smooth muscle is surrounded by connective tissue and is not controlled voluntarily. Cardiac muscle, which makes up the walls of the heart, is striated like skeletal tissue and is involuntary. Each cell has a single nucleus.
4. Antagonistic muscles are muscles that work against one another. Therefore, the contractions of flexors and extensors have opposite effects; extensors open a joint, and flexors close a joint.

STRUCTURES AND FUNCTIONS

1. a, biceps; b, insertion; c, radius; d, ulna; e, origin; f, humerus; g, scapula; h, triceps
2. flexor: bicep; extensor: triceps
3. Insertion of *a* is the radius. Origin of *a* is the scapula.

Section 45-4

VOCABULARY REVIEW

1. Exocrine glands release secretions through ducts.
2. Melanin is a pigment produced by cells in the lower layers of the epidermis.
3. Sebum is a fatty substance secreted by oil glands that helps soften and waterproof skin.
4. Keratin is a protein in skin, hair, and nails.
5. Sweat glands function as excretory organs through the release of excess water, salts, and urea. They regulate body temperature by releasing sweat, which cools the body when it evaporates.

MULTIPLE CHOICE

1. c   **2.** b   **3.** a   **4.** b   **5.** c

SHORT ANSWER

1. It is a barrier that protects the body, retains body fluid, protects against disease, eliminates waste products, and regulates body temperature.
2. It causes skin damage, which causes an increase in melanin production.
3. The epidermis is the outer barrier of the skin and is the first defense against disease, water loss, and ultraviolet radiation damage.
4. Both have clusters of root or base cells, contain dead cells, and have cells that are filled with keratin.
5. Concentrated melanin production in certain areas of the skin causes moles and freckles.

STRUCTURES AND FUNCTIONS

1. a, epidermis; b, dermis; c, muscle fibers; d, blood vessel; e, oil gland; f, pore; g, hair; h, hair follicle; i, sweat gland
2. The epidermis and hair contain keratin.
3. The dermis contains various kinds of sensory neurons that respond to signals, such as heat and pressure.

Section 46-1

VOCABULARY REVIEW

1. Each side of the heart is divided into an upper chamber (an atrium) and a lower chamber (a ventricle).
2. The sinoatrial node sends electrical impulses to the atrioventricular node, which then relays electrical impulses to the muscles of the ventricles and causes them to contract.
3. Arteries are large, muscular vessels that carry blood away from the heart. Veins carry blood to the heart.
4. In pulmonary circulation, blood travels between the heart and lungs. In systemic circulation, blood travels between the heart and other body tissues.

MULTIPLE CHOICE

1. b   **2.** d   **3.** b   **4.** c   **5.** b

SHORT ANSWER

1. Deoxygenated blood moves from the right atrium to the right ventricle and then to the lungs. Oxygenated blood returns from the lungs to the left atrium and then moves into the left ventricle. Oxygenated blood is pumped from the left ventricle and circulates throughout the body. Deoxygenated blood returns to the right atrium.
2. It returns fluids that have collected in the tissues to the bloodstream. It also traps foreign particles, microorganisms, and other tissue debris.
3. Diastolic; if blood flowed back into the left ventricle after contraction, less blood would remain in the arteries, reducing the blood pressure when the heart is relaxed.

STRUCTURES AND FUNCTIONS

1. a, aorta; b, superior vena cava; c, right atrium; d, tricuspid valve; e, right ventricle; f, inferior vena cava; g, pulmonary artery; h, left atrium; i, pulmonary veins; j, mitral valve; k, left ventricle
2. Blood would leak from the left ventricle back into the left atrium, causing reduced systemic blood flow and possible oxygen deficiency.

Section 46-2

VOCABULARY REVIEW

1. Leukocytes help defend the body from disease. Phagocytes are a type of leukocyte that engulf invading microorganisms.
2. An antigen is a protein or carbohydrate that causes the body to produce antibodies, which are defensive proteins.
3. Erythrocytes synthesize large amounts of hemoglobin, which carries oxygen.
4. Platelets are cell fragments involved with blood clotting. Fibrin is a protein that traps red blood cells during clotting.

MULTIPLE CHOICE

1. d   2. c   3. b   4. d   5. c

SHORT ANSWER

1. In the blood, oxygen is bonded to molecules of hemoglobin in red blood cells for transport.
2. Structural differences include: no nucleus in the RBC, but a nucleus in the WBC; one type of RBC, but several types of WBC; and a higher number of RBC in circulation, but a lower number of WBC in circulation. Functional differences include: RBCs transport gases, while WBCs fight diseases; a short life span for RBCs, and a long life span for WBCs.
3. All other blood types contain anti-A or anti-B antibodies. A person with type AB blood will have RBCs with A and B antigens, and mixing anti-A or anti-B antibodies with type AB blood would be harmful.
4. Platelets congregate at a damaged site, sticking together and forming a small plug. Platelets release clotting factors, which begin a series of reactions to produce fibrin. Fibrin produces a net that traps other cells and forms a clot.
5. Because hemoglobin requires a molecule of iron to complete its formation, lack of dietary iron might impair the synthesis of hemoglobin. Hemoglobin carries oxygen; therefore, lack of hemoglobin could impair the oxygen carrying capacity of blood.

STRUCTURES AND FUNCTIONS

1. Type O blood does not contain antigens that would react with any antibodies that the recipient might have.
2. Antibodies to antigens A and Rh will cause agglutination, resulting in blocked vessels in the recipient's body.

Section 46-3

VOCABULARY REVIEW

1. When food is swallowed, the epiglottis covers the trachea. During inspiration, the epiglottis allows air to pass into the trachea.
2. Vocal sounds are produced when air is expired past the vocal chords in the larynx.
3. The trachea branches into two bronchi, each of which leads to a lung. Bronchi branch into smaller tubes called bronchioles.
4. Alveoli are filled with air during inspiration.

MULTIPLE CHOICE

1. d   2. c   3. d   4. b   5. c

SHORT ANSWER

1. Yes; it conducts air between the external environment and the lungs.
2. Most CO_2 is transported as bicarbonate ions. When CO_2 diffuses into plasma, it interacts with an enzyme that converts CO_2 to carbonic acid. The carbonic acid spontaneously breaks down to bicarbonate ions and a proton. Bicarbonate ions are very soluble in the plasma. About a quarter of CO_2 is bound to hemoglobin.
3. The ribs are important for expiration. The muscles between the ribs relax during expiration permitting the ribs to fall. As a result, the thoracic cavity decreases in volume.
4. One possible cause is poor oxygen delivery to cells because of red blood cell deficiency. Other possibilities include impaired blood circulation, defective hemoglobin (sickle cell anemia), damaged lungs, heart, or diaphragm (emphysema), fluid in the alveoli (pneumonia), and living at a very high altitude.

STRUCTURES AND FUNCTIONS

1. concentration gradients
2. CO_2 is more concentrated in the blood. This causes CO_2 to flow from the blood to the lungs and out of the body.
3. No; oxygen and CO_2 each have a concentration gradient. Thus, exchange of one gas is independent of the other.

Section 47-1

VOCABULARY REVIEW

1. Koch's postulates are rules for determining the cause of a given disease.
2. Interferon is a protein produced by virally infected cells. It inhibits the reproduction of viruses by stimulating neighboring cells to produce protein that helps them resist viral infection.
3. Histamine is a chemical messenger that increases blood flow to an injured area and increases the permeability of the surrounding capillaries.
4. Natural killer cells are large white blood cells that attack cells that have been infected by pathogens.

MULTIPLE CHOICE

1. b   2. c   3. d   4. d   5. b

SHORT ANSWER

1. Neutrophils infiltrate damaged areas and engulf invading pathogens.
2. Interferon inhibits the reproduction of viruses by stimulating neighboring cells to produce protein that helps them resist viral infection.
3. The first line of defense includes the skin and mucous membranes. Mucous membranes protect interior surfaces of the body by secreting mucus, a sticky fluid that traps pathogens. Skin serves as a physical barrier to pathogens.
4. Moderate fever stimulates the body's defense mechanisms by suppressing growth of some bacteria and promoting the action of some white blood cells. Thus, taking aspirin to reduce fever could slow the recovery.

STRUCTURES AND FUNCTIONS

1. from top to bottom, 2, 5, 1, 4, 3
2. It permits neutrophils to squeeze through the capillary walls to reach the site of an infection.

3. The cold ice would cause constriction of blood vessels and therefore inhibit blood flow to a wounded area. Thus, the flow of white blood cells to the area would be reduced, and the inflammatory response would be suppressed.

Section 47-2

VOCABULARY REVIEW

1. A plasma cell is a specialized cell that arises from a B cell and produces antibodies.
2. An antigen is any substance that the immune system does not recognize as part of the body and that provokes an immune response.
3. Memory cells are T cells and B cells that don't respond the first time they are exposed to a pathogen but will recognize and attack it during later infections.
4. Antibodies are defensive proteins that attach to specific antigens and inactivate them or trigger their destruction by nonspecific defenses.
5. Allergy is an immune response to a harmless antigen that results in harm to the allergic individual.

MULTIPLE CHOICE

1. c   2. c   3. a   4. b   5. b

SHORT ANSWER

1. When a macrophage that displays a pathogen's antigen on its surface binds to a helper T cell with a receptor matching the antigen, interleukin is released and T cells divide.
2. Vaccines contain the antigens of dead or weakened pathogens. The vaccine causes an immune response and the production of memory cells, which protect the individual from the disease.
3. Antibodies attach to viral surface proteins and prevent the virus from entering host cells and reproducing. Antibodies also cause viruses to clump together, which helps macrophages to engulf the pathogens.
4. T cells would be the cause because if helper T cells are not activated to secrete interleukins, the cytotoxic T cells and B cells will not become activated.

STRUCTURES AND FUNCTIONS

1. a, macrophage; b, helper T cell; c, B cell; d, antigen; e, infected cell; f, cytotoxic T cell; g, antibody; h, plasma cell
2. exposure to a pathogen and production of interleukin-1 and interleukin-2
3. An enzyme that destroys cytokines could destroy interleukin-1 and interleukin-2. Such an enzyme would inhibit the immune response.

Section 47-3

VOCABULARY REVIEW

1. Helper T cells are infected by HIV. The onset of AIDS occurs when the number of helper T cells falls below 200/mL of blood.
2. HIV is the cause of AIDS.
3. Opportunistic infection are infections that are usually stopped by a healthy immune system but succeed when the immune system is impaired, as in the case of AIDS.

MULTIPLE CHOICE

1. c   2. c   3. a   4. c   5. b

SHORT ANSWER

1. No; most AIDS patients die from opportunistic infections.
2. Yes; the immune system is able to combat HIV initially. This period of infection without symptoms may last up to 10 years following infection.
3. transfer of body fluids through sexual contact, sharing hypodermic syringes, and transfer of fluids between mother and fetus or infant
4. Yes; HIV particles or infected cells may be found within the transplanted organs or skin grafts. This risk is known, and donor organs and grafts are tested for HIV.

STRUCTURES AND FUNCTIONS

1. AIDS began six years after infection.
2. The number of helper T cells has decreased so much that plasma cells can no longer be stimulated to produce HIV antibody.

Section 48-1

VOCABULARY REVIEW

1. The six basic nutrients are carbohydrates, proteins, lipids, vitamins, minerals, and water.
2. An unsaturated fat is a fatty acid that has at least one double bond between carbon atoms.
3. Vitamins function as coenzymes; that is, they activate enzymes and help them function.
4. Dehydration causes the fluid volume of the body to decrease. Water moves from intercellular spaces to blood by osmosis. Eventually water is drawn from the cells. As water is drawn, the cytoplasm becomes more concentrated until the cell can no longer function. Dehydration also impairs the body's ability to regulate its temperature.

MULTIPLE CHOICE

1. d   2. a   3. d   4. c   5. c

SHORT ANSWER

1. Essential amino acids are those amino acids that must be obtained from food. Nonessential amino acids can be produced by the body.
2. Simple sugars are important because they represent the final carbohydrate that must be formed before it can be used for energy production.
3. Water is important because it is a medium for chemical reactions, it constitutes 90% of blood volume, it is used in waste removal, and it helps regulate body temperature.
4. Nutrients are required for proper function and growth.

STRUCTURES AND FUNCTIONS

1. group a, the carbohydrates
2. group c, animal products. No, essential amino acids are also obtained from plant products and legumes.

Section 48-2

VOCABULARY REVIEW

1. The pharynx serves as a passageway for air to the trachea and food to the esophagus. The epiglottis is a flap that prevents food from entering the trachea during swallowing.

2. An ulcer can develop when the mucous coating of the stomach breaks down, allowing the enzymes contained in gastric fluid to eat through the stomach lining.
3. Peristalsis moves digested material into the colon.
4. The pyloric sphincter, a circular muscle between the stomach and small intestine, regulates the flow of chyme, digested material formed by the stomach, from the stomach to the small intestine.
5. The gastrointestinal tract includes the small intestine, which is lined with numerous villi where absorption of nutrients occurs.

MULTIPLE CHOICE

1. b   2. d   3. b   4. c   5. c

SHORT ANSWER

1. Mucus protects the stomach's inner lining from digestive secretions.
2. Pepsin, an enzyme, catalyzes the breakdown of proteins to peptides.
3. The pancreas secretes pancreatic fluid into the small intestine. Pancreatic fluid neutralizes stomach acid and has enzymes that hydrolyze disaccharides into monosaccharides, fats into fatty acids and glycerol, and proteins into amino acids.
4. The richest supply of blood capillaries should be in the walls of the small intestine, specifically the ileum and jejunum. These are the areas where the absorption of the digested nutrients occurs.

STRUCTURES AND FUNCTIONS

1. a, esophagus; b, liver; c, colon; d, rectum; e, mouth; f, stomach; g, small intestine
2. The liver stores glycogen, breaks down toxic substances, and secretes bile, which digests fats.
3. Absorption takes place in the small intestine, where villi and microvilli greatly increase the surface area.

Section 48-3

VOCABULARY REVIEW

1. The nephron is the functional unit of the kidney where urine is produced.
2. The urethra is the tube through which urine passes from the urinary bladder out of the body.
3. The renal medulla is the inner two-thirds of the kidney.
4. Excretion is the process of removing metabolic wastes from the body. Students may also include that during excretion, the metabolic wastes pass through a membrane to leave the body.
5. Urea is a nitrogenous waste that is produced from ammonia by the liver and then is removed by the kidneys.

MULTIPLE CHOICE

1. d   2. c   3. c   4. b   5. d

SHORT ANSWER

1. Filtration is the initial step in urine formation. This is when small compounds, including nitrogenous waste products, are separated from the blood and transferred to the nephron.
2. Kidneys assist in the maintenance of fluid volume, blood pH, and the chemical composition of fluids.

3. The entire renal cortex and medulla are composed of nephrons. Nephrons are considered the functional units of the kidney because they perform all of the processes required for urine production.
4. Ammonia is the first step in the production of urea, which is excreted by kidneys.

STRUCTURES AND FUNCTIONS

1. a, proximal convoluted tubule; b, loop of Henle; c, Bowman's capsule; d, glomerulus; e, distal convoluted tubule; f, collecting duct
2. The filtrate is collected in the Bowman's capsule.
3. filtrate = volume reabsorbed + urine produced; 100 mL filtrate − 99 mL reabsorbed = 1 mL urine produced; 1500 mL urine/day × 100 mL filtrate/1 mL urine = 150,000 mL filtrate/day

Section 49-1

VOCABULARY REVIEW

1. Dendrites are extensions of neurons that receive signals from other neurons.
2. Axon terminals are the ends of axons and may communicate with muscle cells, gland cells, or other neurons.
3. An action potential is the transmission of an electrical impulse along the axon of a neuron.
4. A neurotransmitter is a chemical that is released from axon terminals at synapses and that transmits an electrical signal between neurons.
5. A synapse is the junction where a neuron communicates with another neuron or other type of cell.

MULTIPLE CHOICE

1. c   2. b   3. c   4. d   5. d

SHORT ANSWER

1. A neurotransmitter can either increase or decrease the activity of a postsynaptic neuron, depending on the ion channels that are activated by the neurotransmitter.
2. At resting potential, potassium ions are more concentrated inside the cell, whereas sodium ions are more concentrated outside the cell.
3. Action potentials conduct down an axon away from the cell body and toward the axon terminal because of the refractory period, the period of time during which sodium channels cannot open after an action potential.
4. Because ions cannot pass through the myelin sheath, myelin increases the speed of the action potential because the electrical impulse must "jump" from node to node as it moves down the axon.

STRUCTURES AND FUNCTIONS

1. At the resting potential, voltage-gated sodium channels are not open. Thus, sodium ions cannot diffuse into the neuron.
2. Figure *b* shows the conduction of an action potential down the axon. Sodium ions are flowing into the cell, reversing the polarity of the cell. Potassium ions are rushing out of the cell because their voltage-gated channels are open.
3. Electrical and concentration gradients cause the movement of sodium and potassium ions.

Section 49-2

VOCABULARY REVIEW

1. The brain stem lies below the diencephalon and includes the midbrain, pons, and medulla oblongata. The medulla oblongata serves as a relay center that controls heart rate, respiration rate, and other homeostatic activities.
2. The somatic nervous system and the autonomic nervous system are the two independent components of the motor division of the peripheral nervous system.
3. The central and peripheral nervous systems are the two main divisions of the nervous system and work together to collect and process information and control the body's response to the information.
4. The thalamus and hypothalamus are both part of the diencephalon of the brain. The thalamus relays sensory signals, and the hypothalamus helps maintain homeostasis and controls hormone production..

MULTIPLE CHOICE

1. a   2. b   3. c   4. d   5. c

SHORT ANSWER

1. The limbic system functions in emotion, memory, motivation, and other social behaviors.
2. The ventral roots contain the axons of motor neurons, which carry information away from the central nervous system.
3. In a state of physical or emotional stress, the sympathetic division of the autonomic nervous system redirects blood flow from the digestive system toward the heart and skeletal muscles.
4. The autonomic nervous system is most important for homeostasis because it acts constantly to modulate the body's internal conditions.
5. No; the central and peripheral nervous systems constantly interact. The spinal cord constantly relays information to the brain from the body and from the brain to the body.

STRUCTURES AND FUNCTIONS

1. structure A, the gray matter
2. It would eliminate sensory input to the spinal cord from that spinal nerve.
3. It would eliminate sensory input and motor output to and from the spinal cord from that spinal nerve.

Section 49-3

VOCABULARY REVIEW

1. Papillae are bumps on the tongue between which taste buds are embedded.
2. Rods are photoreceptors in the retina that respond to dim light.
3. The retina is the light-sensitive layer that lines the back of the inside of the eye.
4. Cones are photoreceptors in the retina that respond to bright light of different colors.

MULTIPLE CHOICE

1. c   2. b   3. b   4. b   5. a

SHORT ANSWER

1. Vibrations of the bottom membrane of the cochlea stimulate hair cells in the organ of Corti, triggering action potentials that reach the brain through the auditory nerve.
2. the vibration of the tympanic membrane
3. Light stimulates photoreceptors deep in the retina, which in turn stimulate neurons on the retinal surface. Visual information is then carried through the optic nerve to the thalamus and from the thalamus to the visual cortex of the occipital lobe.
4. In each of these sensory systems, the thalamus acts as a relay of sensory information to the proper regions of the brain where various sensory stimuli are interpreted.
5. Body parts that perceive and interact with the environment receive the most sensory input. Interaction with the environment is crucial to survival. That is, body parts with the most "important" and complex functions are those needed to find food, avoid danger, reproduce, and sense pain and other stimuli.

STRUCTURES AND FUNCTIONS

1. photoreceptors; 2. mechanoreceptors;
3. mechanoreceptors; 4. chemoreceptors;
5. mechanoreceptors; 6. thermoreceptors;
7. chemoreceptors

Section 49-4

VOCABULARY REVIEW

1. A stimulant is a psychoactive drug that alters the nervous system by increasing its activity.
2. Tolerance is a characteristic of drug addiction in which larger doses are required to achieve the desired effect.
3. Addiction produces a dependence on a drug that alters normal functioning of the nervous system to the point that withdrawal is experienced if the drug is removed.
4. Nicotine is the addictive drug in tobacco, the use of which can lead to emphysema, a degenerative lung disease.

MULTIPLE CHOICE

1. c   2. d   3. a   4. b   5. c

SHORT ANSWER

1. Repeated exposure to a drug causes a person to need more and more of the drug to achieve the desired effect. Thus, tolerance increases with repeated use.
2. Symptoms of drug withdrawal include vomiting, headache, insomnia, breathing difficulties, depression, mental instability, and seizures.
3. Cocaine blocks reuptake receptors, inhibiting the reuptake of dopamine from the synaptic cleft. The excess dopamine overstimulates postsynaptic neurons, providing the sensation cocaine users seek.
4. There is an inverse relationship between body weight and BAC. As body weight increases, BAC decreases per number of drinks consumed. People with higher body weights have larger blood volumes. So if two people drink the same amount of alcohol, the alcohol will be less concentrated in the person with the larger volume of blood.

STRUCTURES AND FUNCTIONS

Group A includes throat irritation, heart attack, emphysema, addiction, chronic bronchitis, and tars. Group B includes slows respiratory system, drowsiness, liver damage, fetal alcohol syndrome, and addiction.

Section 50-1

VOCABULARY REVIEW

1. Target cells are specific cells to which a hormone travels to produce a specific effect.
2. A second messenger is a molecule that initiates changes inside a cell in response to the binding of a specific substance to a receptor on the outside of a cell.
3. A prostaglandin is a modified fatty acid that is secreted by most cells and accumulates in areas where tissues are disturbed or injured.
4. A hormone is a substance that is secreted by cells and acts to regulate the activity of other cells in the body.

MULTIPLE CHOICE

1. d   2. c   3. a   4. c   5. c

SHORT ANSWER

1. A first messenger binds to cell surface receptors and stimulates production of a second messenger that is located within the target cell.
2. Hormones are transported in the bloodstream.
3. No; they have ducts and secrete sweat, not hormones.
4. It depends on the enzymes and other proteins that cAMP activates to change the function of the cell.

STRUCTURES AND FUNCTIONS

1. Anti-C antibody prevents the hormone's action.
2. No; the fact that three of the antibodies do not alter the hormone's action is evidence that it is not simply the binding of an antibody that disrupts the action of the hormone.
3. Segment C is probably the receptor binding portion of the hormone.

Section 50-2

VOCABULARY REVIEW

1. The hypothalamus produces hormones that are stored in the pituitary gland or that regulate the pituitary gland's activities. Both structures are located in the brain.
2. Epinephrine and norepinephrine are secreted by the adrenal medulla and regulate the nervous system's response to stress.
3. Follicle-stimulating hormone and luteinizing hormone are secreted by the anterior pituitary and stimulate secretion of sex hormones from the gonads.
4. Insulin is a hormone secreted by the pancreas and regulates blood sugar levels. Diabetes mellitus is a condition in which cells are unable to obtain glucose due to an insulin deficiency.
5. Estrogen and testosterone are steroid sex hormones secreted by the gonads.

MULTIPLE CHOICE

1. d   2. a   3. c   4. d

SHORT ANSWER

1. The thyroid glands secrete calcitonin, which lowers blood levels of calcium, and the parathyroid glands secrete parathyroid hormone, which raises blood levels of calcium.
2. Oxytocin and antidiuretic hormone (ADH), are produced in the hypothalamus by neurosecretory cells. Oxytocin stimulates uterine contractions during childbirth, and ADH stimulates water reabsorption in the kidneys.
3. The TSH level should be above normal because the negative feedback mechanism would attempt to normalize the thyroid hormone levels by increasing stimulation.

STRUCTURES AND FUNCTIONS

1. In Situation 1, the receptors of Cell M are defective. There is no Cell M secretion, indicating that hormone secreted by Cell D is required to stimulate Cell M. Cell D secretion increases due to its attempt to increase the level of Cell M secretion to normal. Both of these responses indicate that Cell D secretes the regulating hormone.
2. In Situation 2, the receptors of Cell D are defective. Cell D secretion is increased because it is unable to detect hormone secreted by Cell M. In response to the increased levels of Cell D hormones, Cell M secretions increase.

Section 51-1

VOCABULARY REVIEW

1. Semen contains sperm and the secretions of three exocrine glands—the seminal vesicles, the bulbourethral glands, and the prostate gland.
2. The testes are the gamete-producing organs of the male reproductive system.
3. Ejaculation is the forceful expulsion of semen from the penis.
4. Seminiferous tubules are the tightly coiled tubules of the testes in which sperm are produced.
5. The epididymis is a long, coiled tubule attached to the testis in which sperm develop.

MULTIPLE CHOICE

1. c   2. c   3. c   4. c   5. d

SHORT ANSWER

1. Sperm move from the seminiferous tubules to the epididymis, through the vas deferens and urethra, and out of the penis.
2. Semen is composed of sperm and secretions from three exocrine glands—the seminal vesicles, bulbourethral glands, and the prostate gland.
3. Seminiferous tubules are located in the testes—the vas deferens is not; there is more than one seminiferous tubule—there is only one vas deferens per testis; seminiferous tubules have meiotic cells in their walls—the vas deferens does not.
4. The sperm's flagellum enables it to swim to an egg, and its head contains digestive enzymes that help it penetrate the egg-s outer layers.
5. Yes; androgens, including testosterone, are required for the successful completion of spermatogenesis. Therefore, it is advantageous that the source of androgens be within the testes to ensure the success of spermatogenesis.

STRUCTURES AND FUNCTIONS

1. a, vas deferens; b, seminiferous tubule; c, epididymis
2. a, mature; b, immature; c, immature

Section 51-2

VOCABULARY REVIEW

1. Ovulation occurs when an ovum, or mature egg, is released from an ovary into the fallopian tube.
2. A woman stops menstruating when her follicles have either ruptured or degenerated. This is called menopause.
3. The uterus is a hollow, muscular organ in which a fertilized egg develops. The lower entrance to the uterus is the cervix, which leads to the vagina and out the body
4. The follicular phase is a stage of the menstrual cycle in which an immature egg completes its first meiotic division.
5. The luteal phase is the stage of the menstrual cycle during which the corpus luteum begins to secrete large amounts of progesterone and estrogen.

MULTIPLE CHOICE

1. a   2. d   3. b   4. c   5. a

SHORT ANSWER

1. Male and female gametes contribute equal numbers of chromosomes to the fertilized egg. Without the diploid number of chromosomes, the fertilized egg usually will not survive.
2. An egg is a round cell, a sperm is an elongated cell; a sperm has a flagellum, an egg does not have a flagellum; a sperm has a midpiece encircled by mitochondria, an egg does not have a midpiece; an egg has a large amount of cytoplasm, a sperm has almost no cytoplasm; an egg is larger than sperm; and a sperm has a condensed elongated nucleus, an egg has a round nucleus.
3. At menopause, most of the follicles have either ruptured or degenerated. Students should be able to deduce that without follicles, there are no eggs.

STRUCTURES AND FUNCTIONS

In figure **a,** FSH stimulates follicular cells within the ovary during the follicular phase of the menstrual cycle. In figure **b,** a corpus luteum within the ovary secretes progesterone during the luteal phase. In figure **c,** the uterine lining sloughs off during menstruation. In figure **d,** an egg is released from an ovarian follicle during ovulation. In figure **e,** estrogen stimulates the reestablishment of the uterine lining during the follicular phase.

Section 51-3

VOCABULARY REVIEW

1. Human chorionic gonadotropin is a hormone secreted by the placenta that stimulates further hormone production in the corpus luteum.
2. Implantation is the beginning of pregnancy when the blastocyst embeds into the uterine lining.
3. Chorionic villi are the part of the placenta that extend into the uterine lining.
4. The umbilical cord consists of fetal arteries and veins that transport nutrients from the mother to the fetus and waste products from the fetus to the mother via the placenta.

5. The fluid-filled amniotic sac surrounds the embryo and cushions it from injury.

MULTIPLE CHOICE

1. c   2. c   3. d   4. b   5. c

SHORT ANSWER

1. Estrogen and progesterone inhibit the secretion of LH and FSH. Without FSH, new follicles do not develop and eggs are not prepared for ovulation.
2. All three structures are involved in the transfer of nutrients and waste products between the fetus and mother. Blood vessels originating from the allantois (one of the four embryonic membranes) extend into the chorionic villi. The combination of the chorionic villi and the portions of the uterine lining into which they extend is called the placenta.
3. Estrogen maintains the uterine lining throughout development, ensuring the protection and nourishment of the fetus.
4. An egg must be fertilized, then the zygote must undergo a series of mitotic divisions (called cleavage) that produce a morula and finally a blastocyst. Buildup of the uterine lining must occur prior to implantation.
5. Human chorionic gonadotropin (HCG); HCG is only produced by the placenta. Consequently, HCG is a pregnancy-specific hormone.

STRUCTURES AND FUNCTIONS

1. a, fallopian tube; b, ovary; c, vagina; d, uterus
2. blastocyst—d; zygote—a; corpus luteum—b; morula—a